Re-Visioning
RAMAKRISHNA

Published by
Sterling Publishers Private Limited

Re-Visioning
RAMAKRISHNA

M. SIVARAMKRISHNA

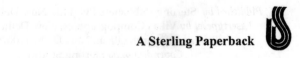

A Sterling Paperback

STERLING PAPERBACKS
An imprint of
Sterling Publishers (P) Ltd.
L-10, Green Park Extension, New Delhi-110016
Ph.: 6191784, 6191785, 6191023 Fax: 91-11-6190028
E-mail: sterlin.gpvb@axcess.net.in
ghai@nde.vsnl.net.in

Re-Visioning RAMAKRISHNA
©1999, M. Sivaramkrishna
ISBN 81 207 2202 7

Published by Sterling Publishers Pvt. Ltd., New Delhi-110016.
Lasertypeset by Vikas Compographics, New Delhi-110029.
Printed at Shagun Offset, New Delhi-110029.
Cover design by Sterling Studio

for
'SRI RAM'
the Envisioned
'SRI RAM'KRISHNA

ACKNOWLEDGEMENT

Thanks cease to be adequate for Shri S.K. Ghai, 'Sterling' publisher of remarkable books on inner life.

Shri Ghai is our creative collaborator and I invoke the good wishes of Ramakrishna and 'Sri Ram' on him, personally and professionally.

M. Sivaramkrishna

WAVE-VISUALS

1

THE PRESENCE

The dark night makes sight dim but imagination is aflame; ignited with the torch of burning, all-consuming love it settles on the Presence in Panchavati. Motionless yet alert; blind to the outer, lighted up in the interior. The body itself is radiant with that luminosity that hurts the eye but heals the heart. It is in that heart that the figure flaps its wings and settles: *bhakter hriday bhagavaner baithakkhana.* One watches it amazed, dumb-struck; as scene after scene is seen in the unseen eye of entrancing, engulfing love. "Come," the figure whispers, breaking its silence, "don't be distant or dazed; I shall re-vision everything for you, child!" I listen but then doubt surfaces. The swan-like figure firmly holds me: "Doubt? Yes, a speck of dust that hurts the eye. Here, let me remove it gently!"

Afraid to allow the touch but aching for it! I seem to shrink in self-conscious shyness: haven't I sinned against everything? I hardly did *japa;* meditate? Virtually no. Chanting and singing? Even listening I did, listlessly. "But haven't you kept me in sight... even when you held the one you love so passionately?" he whispered—the weariness of the mother, the faint listlessness explaining to a retarded child, punishing himself, wafted like a breeze....

"You think I can't see? You imagine you can shield anything from me!" He holds me, this time gently, oh! Ever so gently. The touch-feather: can I put it for you in words? Words, too, shrink: shy brides eager for the touch but engulfed by sheer, benumbing hesitation. The groom is amused!

Holding still, the voice cajoles, caresses. Have you heard the voice doing what touch does? Or touch deputising for the voice? Voice and touch crisscrossing in a moment of eternity that effaces all that is time-bound, all that is space-confined: "If you were a woman..." the words trail off! "See I got the particle of dust that clouds your eye! Come, it is late but not too late; for everything is, in its moment, timely, neither late nor early. The moments just are; Shall I unfold them for you? May I...?"

No words are needed and no reply is awaited. The radiant Beloved settles; the eyes meet; usually half-closed, they now open fully: pools of flaming love, they set out to re-vision for me what all they saw, what all they did, what all they spoke! "Come, dear," (are you afraid if I call you my 'lover'?—she whispered—) "I shall show you things that only you can see!" A tinge of pride, perhaps flitted across. "For any one who loves me!" she said, deflating it.

2

THE FLUTE

Panchavati again: the figure is still: description is futile: evocation is the only thing it permits.

The limpid Ganga flows by. The whisper of the waves sets its rhythms to tune with what the Presence needs. The temple glints in the dark: Bhavatarini is out! She watches without being watched: the *lila kshetra* she created for her child and lover, spreads across that part of the Ganga. Even the boatmen are lost in slumber. They can't ferry any one across in the night. Only Kali, the Black One, can....

I watch entranced; the radiance of the place rends my consciousness—the darkness disappears. All is light. Light that reveals just enough for me to see. Enough for me to dispel the deluding *mahamaya*. Not eternally. Adequate to listen, to look, to love and to be lost in the enchantment before me and the Mother behind me. Suddenly the flash comes: the Dakshineswar Kshetra is the Kudali Sangama: the junction of life and death.

"Do you know," the voice breaks the reverie and asks, "this place is just the one I wanted? And did the Mother fail to give me anything I wanted?" Did he at any time want what the Mother didn't want to give? The Mother is the *yantra*, the devotee is the *yantri*. In my turn, this one is my *yantra* and I am the *yantri*.

"That is right! You are the Flute I want to play on! But then on your hard bamboo I have to bore holes. Then, only then, music fills you; pours into you, enthralls you...." The voice is lost in the words it speaks. The Veda and the Nada merge, moments of *laya*

yoga supreme. I wait expectantly, to listen to this *Ishwara* about
Dakshineswara. But who am I to decide what I should get? The
lilting voice, dances on the Mother's lips, breaks its words and on
the wings of love and takes off into the music of the spheres!
Words cease; the voice rests: "Wait! Open the ear of wordless
music!" And the Words come like startled little birds thrown out
gently from the Mother's nest. The Cosmic Form vomits vowels
and consonants:

Here in Dakshineswara
Hear the song of Death! and the saga of life.
The Tortoise that bears the earth
Rests here;
The cemetery silently
Salutes those who really live!
What intoxicating fragrance
It emits!
Brahmamayi draws breath
here. But
I devour the breath, the
fragrance, the dust, the earth
The bones, the skulls,
The mud and mire,
The gold and silver,
The aged, the young
Men, women
Everything is grist to
My grinding mill!
From the ant, the worm to woman
and beyond!

Afraid even to move, breathless as if *rechaka* and *kumbhaka*
swing into play, I listen. The lolling tongue licks the words
drenched with the nectar of the Deathless One. The nectar
transforms the words: are they words? Matrikas, they are. The
Word that sustains all words and yet is itself wordless, makes the
maya garland, the *varnamala*. With avidity I seize it and adorn my
neck. Every bead, every flower blushes, blossoms and

gets blasted, too
gets dissolved, too
gets devoured...
that lilting refrain completes—the song.

The magic and the music waft on the bosom of the Ganga, and caresses me: "If you want to love the Mother, love me! For your sake I enact the *lila,* the play of Kali. But do you know what I did this time? I, myself, donned a role, not just direct the play!".

I explode into irrepressible laughter. Joy courses through the veins; the body registers the truth. For our sake if She wants to play, what fun to play along! Is there sorrow in a play? It dips you like the *jilepi* in the *rasa* but deters all attempts at annihilating the taste and the taster twins. I would, in turn, taste the Presence and not get drowned in it. Taste and surface again, to tell myself what the Presence shows me.

3

LOVING THE ONE WHO DELIGHTS IN DESTRUCTION

"Why do we meet only in the night?" I ask. Silence greets me. Perhaps he hears or he does not. The words go into the void. Frightening quiet reigns. Even the cicadas are quiet. You could even cut into the silence with a knife—as Chinnamasta cuts her own head!

Slowly, almost inaudibly, a sound begins. From where, I cannot say. All that I am aware of is the Presence before me. And that is hardly awake. A serene smile lights up the face like a lamp in a windless place, it sheds light all around. The sound is now much more distinct—it seems now a rhythm. "Seem" for you could only "see" the Presence and from that the rhythm emerges.

The rhythm now acquires—a gait, a lilt, and a momentum. Similar to strokes on a drum, barely heard in the beginning, are now much stronger.

Panchavati lies hushed in a daze. No creature stirs, none dares even to breathe, I suppose. The Ganga touches the banks-curiously, inquisitively but withdraws discreetly. The stars glinting through the thick leaves of the dense trees dare not sparkle. Awed and startled, they hang in the sky, witness to the *lila*.

Suddenly I notice a change. The rhythms of the sound are now insistent, almost feverish. The pitch is something, if you are not used to it, deafening. But the music of the primal sound continues in the midst of the ear-splitting sounds. Fear is swept away by wonder. Wonder that the ears could receive without getting shattered. Wonder that one could remain so silent and yet not feel petrified. The sound sinks into barely coherent words:

The One who
Delights in destruction,
Digests whole worlds
In a single bite,
Dazes those who
Set out to know
Her secret;
Dances on the
Letters of Her own making,
Rushing in to
Rescue the letter
From *pralaya!*

Do I dare to put it in words? How much daring a puny creature can have? Cutting through the reverie the sound is now a devouring monster—thousands and thousands of drums beating madly, wildly with no hand seen that beats the drums...? Crazed, now, with fear reducing the body to a cold clod of the earth! The *nada* making one *nadaan:* crazy. The ear can hardly remain intact. Its drums reach the breaking point....

Figures appear everywhere around—shrieking, shouting, wailing, gloating, terrified, serene, mutilated—some with no skulls, others with no bodies. Panchavati is now literally the dancing ground of faces of all colours, shapes and sizes. Ferocious dogs tear at the flesh of the humans with glee. Running for life, they run into a huge monstrous figure with breasts hanging loose from too much sucking, with fiery blood-shot eyes, shouting weirdly, gathering everyone.... Those who rush in with frenzy, crazed with fear, enter the mouth of the Figure. With what relish She masticates! Horror strikes me like a whiplash and I sense I cannot bear it any more....

"And yet you want to love me?" the Presence speaks. Serene, with a mischievous twinkle in her eyes. She seems needlessly amused. "If only you saw...." I look around and see that nothing can be seen. The stars seem to explode into twinkling laughter.

Panchavati lies hushed in silence. Not a creature stirs. Nature's beat seems normal: the primal *pranayama* of her *virat swarupa* flows evenly, tranquil, sedate and stable.

"You cannot love me unless you love the Mother," the Presence speaks amused at what I fail to see. I remain silent-discreet silence, you can say, for, to draw Her out is not easy. What with Her moods....

"Do you know the wrench I feel for Her? Even if you guess, can you put it in words? What, after all, are words? Her *ucchista*. And if She herself stifles you, how can you spit out the words," the Presence continues....

"Then, what about all that I saw? Is it merely a dream?" I venture to voice my twilight uneasiness

"You think a dream is a delusion?" the Presence smiles with those pearly teeth, barely visible. Dazzlingly white, the teeth entrance me. The ash-coated white body of the Lord of Pralaya flashes before my eye. "Dream is no delusion, dear!" the voice continues. "Once you get rid of the delusion, a dream is a vision. And getting rid of the delusion is the Mother's wish. Nothing is in your hands!" "Not even in your hands?" "Of course not," instantly comes the retort. That plunges me into despair, into depression; tears begin to gather....

"That you got this experience is no small matter. You think you are ripe for the vision? You feel that you know what is good for you? Only the Mother knows when and where and what suits you, what you can relish and digest...." A far-away look enters those lovable eyes. Eyes that seem to penetrate the thick layers of time, the *kalamukha* that the Mother Kali can look into. Look into without a blink of the eyelids, without ever closing her eyes.

"Dear! You know my father, too, got filled with fear in Gaya! Such a noble being, guileless, upright, a rose without a thorn. When the Lord entered his being and announced his advent, even in a dream he thought he was unworthy!"

"Even the dream experience made him uneasy about his unworthiness. That he thought of his unworthiness and not about what you think as the unreality of what you saw.... Do you get the difference? Not that it was a dream but that he was not a worthy vehicle for my descent... even in a dream...."

The Presence is, I realise, with a shudder, just not there. A ball of light, an uncanny luminiscence fills the space, floats in the *akasha* and the *chidakasha*. Spreads across everything: the Panchavati, the temples, the river, the stirring beings in the dawn boats getting ready to ford the pilgrims, nearby factories, and still-sleeping city.... Blinking, with eyelids heavy, with the body still shuddering.... I stare into space, into nothingness. I register the forms around me slowly. Then a gentle laughter fills the sky; ripples of inexpressible joy course through my veins. The shivering body shakes off its tension; a sense of utter well-being pours into every nerve....

4

ALL WHO LOVE...

"Why she does not appear during the day? Is that not what you are bothered about?" The Presence cuts through my reverie, yet to articulate itself. No need for that, I know. But I forget quite often. I remain silent.

"You, yourself, have the answer!" A relaxed pause: neither eager to know the answer nor unwilling to accept it if it does not come at all. And I know when you are least expectant, ecstasy fills you and floats across your consciousness. It induces, instantly, stillness without strain, relaxation without reverie. An instant of alertness and peace....

"Do not address me in different ways? The Presence you call me often; She or he you name me; and you are also in love with my name and form: "Ramakrishna" you call me in those moments of exquisite togetherness, moments that merge into moment-less momentous, Now. You know what I experience when you call me "Ramakrishna?" Are you shy to listen to what I achingly experience by that name?"

Yes, of course, I am; shy beyond belief. Self-conscious (not conscious of the Self, that is), to the point of wishing for vanishing from the other's sight. "It's like a Beloved baring her body, willingly, wantonly, ecstatically for the touch of the long, languishing lover lost in loneliness, lost in visions of that whole being. The being which is beyond, but is also the body."

Horripilations shake my body. How could She guess what I thought was private and personal? Not just guess: it was as if She had enjoyed and not I. As if She consumed my whole being and emerged from its ashes, triumphant, radiant, gloating over the extinction.

"Why are you surprised? All who love and make love: aren't they my own Self? Through all the bodies I sport; through all the minds I think, feel, agonise and enjoy. The universe? My antennae, filled with the power of *spanda*! With the touch of a button-forged in the smithy of my love—I make them dance in life, dance their way into exhilarating annihilation. Night for you is blazing light for me...."

5

THE SQUIRREL

The whole day I reel, as it were, under the intoxication of the Presence. The Siva temples, the Radhakanta temple... all are imbued with a radiance I hardly notice earlier. Everyone moving around seems bathed in the sheer splendour of the Mother. Even the dogs (what arrogance using the word "even"!) seem frisking about in pleasure. And Bhavatarini? Eager, expectant to ford them across: from seif-imposed misery and sorrow to bliss, to the joy of the paradoxes of life and death. "Follow me and commune with me: you are Siva. Desert me, disregard me you are Shava, trampled under my feet, throttled out of existence," she seems to whisper.

Ganga smiles at her pranks. She herself, she knows, is made to swallow, drown, deluge in hundreds over centuries galore...ever since she jutted out, with ecstasy, from the fiery locks of Siva. But she quenches the thirst-of millions over aeons. A dip is exhilarating; a drop is purifying. Ganga mayi! A sprinkle is enough to disinfect the depraved, the decadent, the dispossessed.

"Yes, dear, Ganga is incomparably pure, intoxicatingly bracing, I know," the Presence startles me with her voice. When did the day end? How did I come here, again, into this field every particle of which dances with ecstasy forbearing on its bosom the lilting, dancing feet of "Ramakrishna". Panchavati: has any other place seen as many splendours, as many wonders as she did? Can one see them without a sharp pang of pain and pleasure benumbing the body? Can one touch her without getting electrified with ecstasy? She saw things that no human eye dares to see unless the eye is touched with transforming love. The past is locked in her folds with the key of love!

"How glibly you talk of love, babu!" the words pierce into my flesh. Yes, talk is the only thing I did. I prided myself with my facility with *sabda*. *Sabda* hardly crossed the threshold of the alphabet. The frame was frozen for long: the tongue chained to the delusion of speech. I look at the Presence distraught, helpless, stricken with the paralysis of speech. It needs to be numbed: lies numberless, metaphors meaningless; similes sterile; sentences that were decked with ornaments while the body is a corpse!

"Do you know how long I waited for you to come back! Waiting is the only thing I am good at! That is why Sabari is so dear to me. I waited like her like a rock immune to weather, impervious to time, intractable to the very rhythms of change and decay and growth and bloom! Winters I weathered, summers passed me by; spring's delight I forfeited! Waiting, waiting, endless, expectant, agonising. But what intoxication waiting for you to come back!"

Tears streaming down her cheeks! Can anyone wait like this? Is it, let alone possible, credible? Is such love conceivable? What does she gain by gaining my love? Does the ocean feel any difference if a drop gets added to her immensity? "Your love? How foolish, how naive you are!" She chuckles. "Did the Mother hook me with her harp of love thinking I am just a queer fish in her ocean of *samsara*? Certainly not! Every fish belongs to her ocean but...."

He hesitates, seems lost in *bhava*. What crosses in his *chaitanya:* how do we know? The rhythms of silence and speech dance with the ebb and tide of the river. A small squirrel runs into the thick of the jungle that is Panchavati. How lucky that it carries a permanent mark of the touch on its back that is transforming timelessness! Have we anything comparable to show?

A deep sigh... as if the pain is too deep for the flesh to bear." "I do not know even now," he speaks haltingly.... "I doubt whether you got really tired of the toys I gave you to play with, to amuse yourself. How quickly you forget amusing oneself is a form of musing on the Mother? How engrossed you become with toys!"

"You should not have given us toys at all," words escape my lips instinctively. She seems surprised-pleased at a precocious child pulling back his tongue from silence. First time that night she laughs, a laugh that somebody told me is called *"smita"*, subdued, amused, with a touch, just a touch of compassion without condescension.

"I know, I shouldn't have. But what can I do: I am myself fond of toys. Don't you know...?" Yes. I know. What marvels of toys, of clay models he made. Your eyes get glued; they jump out of their sockets in disbelief at such evident dance of consciousness: *chaitanya nritya.* "But I also break them; often I mend them before Kali devours them...," he muses. "I like to play, don't make any mistake about it," the firmness in the voice surprises me.

"Recall how one gets attached to toys: not knowing that oneself is one! That lady got attached to an image and I had to mend it, don't you remember?" "Can I forget" "So...," "You don't get me, except as a toy, until you get rid of all the other toys." He nearly snaps. I almost jump. "That's good!" Uncontrollable laughter explodes. Then sudden frightening seriousness crosses the face. The eyes are red with real anger: I nearly turn my face away:

Look at me! Do you
Think it is a joke
To love me?

The words like live coals burn into my heart that nothing can reduce to embers. I am the squirrel now!

6

RAVING ABOUT THE UNREACHABLE

After that, uneasiness unnerves me. The fiery eyes haunt me. I realise that the Presence has another face. Not *soumya* at all. Fear grips me. Memories of the wrongs done, right things not done engulf me. See how many times "me" surfaces! I seem to lose grace, forfeit her trust. "Unworthy! You are unworthy to receive her love!" Like smoke surrounding everything, mist moving across everything.... Nothing is visible. *Dhuma,* smoke opens its ponderous jaws and I drift, dazed, lost in grotesque, weird, unnerving eye-scalding forms of fire that emerge from the smoke.

Oh, Mother! Are you playing your usual tricks? Am I the butt of your joke? A *pipilika* crushed beneath your blessed feet? Are you so perverse as not to spare even those who glimpse your being, come near to taste it? Who said you give *abhaya*? Freedom from fear? You are, yourself, fearful! It is all a fraud, a fiasco, fun, a fib told by countless generations of deluded devotees!

Anger beyond endurance grips me. Seething like a cauldron with no hole for the heat to escape. The cauldron seems to be poised for explosion, reducing all the heated water thirsting for it, to vapour. I no longer watch it from a distance: I am the furnace, the cauldron, the smoke of the fire, the heat of the logs of wood.

And scenes that no one can see and survive, or even imagine grip the eyes like so many needles thrust into them. Yet, the needles bore holes in the cauldron that reveal windows that open to wonders....Wherever I "see" exuberant life asserts itself. Couples copulating in sheer, benumbing lust turn into beings that are ecstatically watching and participating in the vast, unending *lila* of her creation.

How filled she is with ecstasy! Gloating over the glorious, irrepressible saga of creation; of *srishti* that makes her play endlessly on the *vina* with the three notes: *srishti, sthiti, laya.* The face, reeling with the flush of fulfilled love, is entrancing—even the trance has nothing to convey as a word. Wordless is the wonder, sightless is the *drishya.*

Do you know how many are born, live and die or are dying live forever in that act of primal creation? All my creation is an immaculate conception. The seed, I am; the child tearing through my body, I am; the frisking, frolicking girl, I am; her womb is my replica. The womb vomits forth endlessly, with hope against hope; the child should know she is in my womb. How I wait for them to know this! That they don't fall from the womb to the earth? That they rise from the earth to the womb?"

Oh! My! I never realise he too is watching. Why this unnerving trick of materialising from nowhere? "As a concession to your blindness," he answers with mischievous eyes. That is enough for me to explode: "How can we know when you perversely prevent us from knowing?" The twinkle in the eye becomes brighter: "Come on! Let off all the steam! You seem to have boiled long enough! Come, I am in a mood to listen!"

"Then listen. And you better listen carefully." "I am always careful, dear," he whispers. Caring a fig for whispers and gestures, I continue, "Love me! You shout. We look around to love you but all that we see is nothing lovable. Then why not I love the body visible when the body—the *virat swarupa,* you grandly call it—is not to be seen anywhere. Why not reach out for what is within reach rather than rave about the unreachable Ramakrishna? Why not enjoy this rather than that?" I pause for breath, heaving for space, for breath to regulate itself.

The twinkle is "toned" down. Just a little trace of sadness appears. Quickly in a split second sadness sinks into the being, as it surfaces. So is it swallowed. Not an expert in *mudra* stuff. I silently look at it. "Have you done with your explosion? At least for the present?" Not caring for words any longer, I simply look at the Presence....

7

SAMSARA IS NIRVANA

The sky is threateningly close. Birds fly across with a grace dancers can take a few tips from. How I wish I fly with them into a space that has nothing to confine, to restrain, to inhibit! What joy to be floating in space! Floating, wherever you like, with no one watching and warning you, threatening to clip your soaring wings.

Birds are not told to: "Do this, don't do that." Hovering over the ocean, they swoop in a second and snatch a fish. That is enough. They don't need ethics. Nobody tells them "this fish is mine, that is yours! So keep away from mine!" but look at the angler: She catches fish, puts them in her basket and none can touch her basket.

The river, too, allows fish to be caught. Whether bird, man or beast nothing seems to matter. On her vast expanse, on her heaving bosom, anyone can swim, any boat can ply. She floats them, she ferries them across, the Bhavatarini, the ford spanning the oceans of samsara and nirvana.

"*Samsara* is *nirvana,* dear!" She gently reminds. "Not *samsara* and *nirvana*." I listen but continue the silence—that lens that can look beyond and behind, before and after. Moments of utter ease, of inexplicable calm clip the wings of unrest. All passion not spent but smouldering like slowly dying sparks of fire—just that glint of warmth to prevent cold. Just enough heat to ignite, if needed:

Nothing to gain; for
Nothing is lost;

Nothing to snatch; for
Nothing is taken away;
Nothing to grieve for; for
Nothing is enjoyed;
The sky doesn't shrivel
Because you fly across;
The earth doesn't shrink
Because you trample on it;
The river is not riven
Because you row across;
The wind doesn't stop blowing
Because your skin arrests it;
The fire is not extinguished
Because your embers are extinct
The sun doesn't stop beaming
Because you close your windows.
Love doesn't stop loving
Because you think you lost yours!

A benumbing cry of pain snaps at me: She is writhing in waves of intolerable agony. Marks of a whiplash slowly, imperceptibly, surface to bleed; that seem to ooze drops of exquisite, relishable and relished agony. I look around: nonplussed, stupid with witless incomprehension. A hissing sound like a serpent beaten on the back—endlessly, repeatedly... the image registers.

And the eye sees another: two fishermen, bleeding with injuries on the back inflicted mutually, slowly land on the bank of the river at a distance. Their women are seething with impotent anger: "You always beat each other! Oh ma! When will they know...." The words trail off. She chuckles and looks at me. Enough fish... for everyone, for anyone.

8

LILA VINODINI

The sound of the anklets seeps into the twilight. Neither asleep nor awake, I lie on the ground. Hallowed by her feet, the ground receives me with warmth. A crazy sense of being lulled to sleep, by her, invades me. Many lie around; snoring in abandon, resting after hard labour, they seem so many sunflowers wilted but waiting for the morrow. I know they will frisk and frolic again; suffer and weep, beat and get beaten; in between make love, lose consciousness, slip into oblivion. Labourers, devotees, fishermen, women, pilgrims, children, slipping into sleep even while sucking at mother's breasts, half exposed. On the banks, inside the courtyard, wherever there is space, wherever they are permitted, suffering mutely, with not much to call their own....

The reverie is broken: the jingle of bangles, the *anahata* of the anklets drags me from drooping and drowsing. Who is there who is awake when everyone is asleep! Whose is that soft fall of footsteps, that unearthly *laya,* that interiorly audible sound that moves in grace! Grace not seen clearly but felt in the guts like a gentle prodding of the coiled serpent. "You sleep light! That is good!"

Energy courses through the spine flooding the crevices. Tingling sensation teases the body. Inert a few moments ago, it moves now with incredible bounce. Not jumping but creeping slowly, steadily, dragged and drugged by her. Drugged by the music but not drowned. She wants me to see what she wants to show. Do I have wants of my own? Of late, nothing seems mine!

"Allow me to lead you," she seems to plead. "You thought you led yourself—for far too long. Now I will lead you...." Do I have to reply? Bagalamukhi restrains my speech. I forfeit speech but find her.

Through the "I"
Of the camera
My "eye" sees!
See with me!
Be yours!

Can I bear the grafting? Will I be able to live after that? "Are you living now?" she laughs, amused. The laughter fills—the skies, the river, the gardens, the temple, the factories, the cemeteries—all *akasha,* all *prithvi* shrinks to swallow and glow in that laughter!

I find myself on the steps that lead to the *sikhara* of the temple. Ganga gleams below: unfathomable mystery lies in her timeless waters. The sky is overcast. Past midnight, stars are blotted out. How dare they see what she doesn't want them to see! Like frightened children they hide in the clouds, peering at the edges. Afraid to see but daring to.... What is there that she holds from us....

My eyes are now smeared with the black of her blackness. Not all the perfumes of blackness can blacken her: She is black herself. Strange magic makes the eyes bloom like lotuses lying in the mud but laying traps for the bees that roam for love-nectar. Sheer inexplicable madness fills the eyes.

Gently she ascends
The steps to the
Terrace, of the temple, gently
As if the steps
Are so many live
Coals of consciousness:
Mrinmaya is chinmaya!

I lie in ambush a few steps below. She walks on the terrace looking at her city: Kali is the city; the city is Kali. She surveys everything around: with infinite joy at the animate toys sunk in slumber, her *kalaratri,* the primal night, that swallows everything like so many ants entering the mouth of the Kaliya, the Serpent on which she dances in glee, the serpent she tamed. The serpent that lies coiled at her bidding, but uncoiling when she touches it with her lolling tongue still tasting the tingling sensation of warm blood!

Strange! Without fear, *sandeha,* suspicion, bereft of shame, I see her naked striding across the terrace. The earth itself is her cloak: how can she be naked? Born naked we lie buried, naked. Born into her lap from the four walls of her womb, naked, how pitifully we try to dress ourselves! She walks with ecstasy. See how her steps falter, intoxicated with the majesty of her own creation! She is *lila vinodini,* the enjoyer of her own play, inhabiting every nook and corner of her mansion of mirth:

In the lotus
Of my heart
Her full figure
Blooms in unearthly
Splendour!
The gods are dazed;
Humans lie blissfully
In the garland of
Skulls, drinking,
In those cups, the
nectar of her Being.
She feeds them
Fondly, winking at
Her suckling children!

I gaze and gaze glued to her glorious Presence, gloating at the grace that gives this glimpse that eyes cannot see without losing their sight. But, then, what I see in a split second is stranger still!

Who is he
Who walks unsteadily
Reeling in *rasa*!
The eyes are half-open, drunken
And do not seem to see—
anything.

A dazzling smile,
Smile that drugs
And drags you
By the tail like
A serpent being
Dragged but drugged
In yielding surrender;
Smiles at his pranks!
In utter, unconscious —
Abandon, he tears the
Clothes, throws them to the
Winds!
The Digambara,
The four directions his full dress
What does he need
For another mask!
"Ma, Ma!" the
only sound that
soundlessly, rhythmically
courses through
the hamsa, the
celestial swan,
swimming in the
waters of weightless,
windless consciousness.
I blink in disbelief! "Where is She?" Has she done the
vanishing trick again? Who is this Presence?
You need
Bifocals child!
I am the mother
The mother says
"Is there any
difference?"
In adoration tears like pearls suffuse my face!

9

SEE THE COTTON INSIDE

Restless through the day, I desperately seek the solacing arms of the night. The Presence plays hide and seek. I see him somewhere around but going there is futile. There is only emptiness to greet me. Voices break the mood. Nothing registers, however, Everything is empty, a frightening void.

Have you faced this at any time? Then you will know. Utter, inexplicable inertia engulfs me like a tidal wave. The eye is scalded with the cataract of total incoherence. I can hardly recognise anything around. Covered with fog, the landscape lies low, lost in the caverns of the earth. Not even guilt (bosom companion) glints in the glistening collyrium that paints the eyes of everything.

Not even memories are left to play with or pine for. Perhaps total annihilation could be like this. I sit on the edge of a stone that conceals someone who, perhaps, lived and loved and languished. Drifted into the arms of the Mother, drifted without fear, without faith, without even the least trace of the desire to survive. "He who welcomes the Mother welcomes annihilation...." A faint,-first stirring-of something felt before, flashes.

I follow the flash, a ray of light, bright enough to pave a path. The path is paved with the stones of sorrow and suffering, don't you know that? "Give me the one who is unhappy!" An echo, I heard before floods, the being. The faint heart fuels itself, a little.... The light of the solitary ray and the fuel just smouldering but ready to blaze forth, I find them beckoning to me. "Quick!

Follow the light!" they seem to hiss with impatience, with
annoyance.

"Do you know where we are going now?" the voice of the
Presence cuts through the confusion. Should I know? Does
knowing make a difference? How has such a knowing made
anyone the wiser for that knowing? The knowing that knows not
itself is futile. The knowing that knows itself, too, is a chimera.
The knowing that knows that all that needs to be known is beyond
all modes of knowing... for it is already known!

"Oh! Caught again in your usual web of words, the jungle and
jingle of words. I thought you laid them to rest, that you don't need
their aid?" What do I care about what the Presence thought? Has
she at any time snapped with her sword the sorrow of anyone? She
beckons to them and like moths they enter the blazing fire of her
being! She gloats over the prey, perverse beyond patience....

Rebellious without reason, I seethe with anger. Anger that is
helpless, impotent.... Anger that she is so near and yet so far.
Anger that arises from the very awareness that stays and slays.
Why this tantalising sword hung above the head? Why does she
not sever the head and be done with it? Why this illusion of the
sword becoming the flute, or the bed of arrows turning into soft
feathers of her lovely lap.

"Do you think it is my doing?" she challenges. "Do you
imagine that I tease and torture and then drink with abandon the
blood of all that results from this?" An impulse to argue stings like
a bee. But I resist it, I smother it, squash it mercilessly. "That's
good; squash the bees of doubt that sting but do you know bees
save honey for you...." The art of tasting the honey but not getting
stung by the swarm of bees....

"Come! I want to show you something." She pulls me from
the ground gently. Whoever can succeed in putting that touch into
the tool box of *sabdas*, of *vyakarana*, of *alankara*? We seem to
glide on the ground softly, our feet hardly sense the earth. There is
something uncanny about it. Is she up to her *indrajala* again?

We enter a vast landscape through a gate guarded by a
beehive. "Don't disturb them! Enter with the footfall of an ant!"

Admiring the image but annoyed with its incongruence, I do pass
through. A sea-change totally transformative, incredibly
transpositional.

Lakes and trees abound. Frolicking, shouting and chasing
each other...so many people. Benches for the picnickers to sit and
see. Has Panchavati been transplanted all the way... crazy idea.
(But aren't all such experiences crazed?) But where is she?
Suddenly a tingle goes up and down the spine. Consciousness
flaps its wings; like the peacock striding majestically in the
garden, awareness stretches its eye-feathers. It flies through space
and time, across vast stretches of transfigurations. The coiled
consciousness sheds its slumber; hissing with energy flooding its
being, it straightens back and looks across the landscape, looking
for her....

"I am here, *baba*," the voice is familiar but the face is not. It
seems to come from one of those boats in the lake. I peer through
the gathering shadows. Who is this One? Dressed in trousers and a
full-sleeve shirt, his smile too is ravishingly, rapturously familiar.
But where is that *dhoti*-clad Presence, where is that blissfully
naked Mother? Where did they disappear?

This one wears glasses, too. Shielding them from soiled eyes,
his eyes sparkle through the dark glasses—so dark they are.
"Soiled?" I am wrong. The mother cleans the child: nothing that is
soiled to her.

Breathlessly gasping for a clue I grope along. To reach the
boat already crowded. So many! I didn't know so many could be
rowed across. "Always there is an extra seat for the one who
comes late; the prodigal late-comer always has my promise of a
seat in this boat, my heart-beat." Incredible, the transposition! Is
he the original owner of Pushpaka kept gleamingly trim; rowing
this time a boat on earth unlike a ship in the air or sea. So that
many can reach, many can be rowed across; the earth is accessible
more than the sky.

"But are you willing to get in?" he asks gently, almost
inaudibly. Edge of the boat—is his seat as if any time he may
prefer falling into the waters and catching hold of those lying

drowned in the depths. "Are you planning to get in?" You have to listen with the ears of a snake to hear that voice. Most often you miss it. Grand ideas of *sravana* won't help you. He denies that: but the demand is clear: "You can listen to my voice only if you stop hearing other voices. Can you do that?" Could I?

"It is simple," the edge of the boat comes closer. With a glance he silences the others, throws them gently into the vaults of slumber, of dreams... but the glance glowed with love. "Let them slumber for some time. Struggling for too long, they have earned their sleep." "It is simple," he repeats. "For you, yes," I keep the doubt to myself. "For everyone, make no mistake, for everyone," gentle but firm in his word, I feel like a child being spanked even while being kept in her lap.

I look around turning my eyes away: eager to look but afraid to look through those "looking-through-thoroughly" eyes. That gives me confidence. "To get into the boat, you require the Mother, you need Ramakrishna." I pause. It is time to get things straight. He is relaxed; taking out his glasses, he polishes them and puts them away. "Ask anything and I shall give it to you!" seems to be the look in the eyes bereft of coverings. "I haven't seen them: either the Mother or Ramakrishna!" a regret held for long, simmering inside, surfaces.

Tears stream down his cheeks: he sobs as if all the waters of the seven seas have entered, tearing his eyes apart. Uncontrollable, they flow through with no bridge to stop them, nothing to divert the flow. I look amazed, harrowed with fear and wonder. Those tears ebb and tide, breaking the banks I built. Shattering everything I fondly clutch at myself for the fear of being engulfed. All the boats drown and disappear. Shoreless ocean of tears shed unendingly, ever since she ecstatically, erotically, ascetically made herself into the Many. I try holding my head high, mortally afraid of sinking to the depths. Afraid of the whirlpool, of the rushing waters that seem bent, this time, on devouring me.

"Yes, you don't have to seek; you are the sought. The hound of heaven this time covers her hunting urge with glasses." He wipes the tears away. Through the dewdrops of tears, the lotus emerges in radiant light, that plays shimmering, on the tears. My breath regulates itself. It climbs the steps easily, with grace, with nothing that impedes its slow, steady motion.

Illumination floods the *sahasrara* for just a moment that is eternity. And gently comes, over the waves, the caressing voice:

Ramakrishna sees you,
Child; he has come
To show himself. Remove the
Pillow case; see the
Cotton inside!

10

THE LORD OF THE ANIMALS

I hesitate to enter the small room. Quite often he comes home-disguised, an actor painting his face and entering the stage. But an ardent desire to see him in his own habitat. Hauntingly ardent. How does he behave there? How does he look? As I see him outside? With eyes withdrawn, with few words on the lips? Affectionate but... I can't put it across to you. Perhaps, I can see him without a problem, but a glass-sheet prevents touch, proscribes intimacy... allows seeing.

The uproariously shouting voices coming from inside grate on my ears. What a spectacle inside! Mostly young, they are all doubled up with laughter. Some are rolling on the ground clutching their stomachs! The joke he has cracked eludes me. A few in a corner are munching something, like monkeys, looking at him with that naivete writ large on their face which only kids can have. And they are no kids! The average age must be twenty.

Some simply lie near his feet (the feet that Brahma himself washed!). Sleeping, I think. But how wrong! *Nishpanda deha*, someone called it: bodies that are not inert but intriguingly irresponsive. Alert to him, alien to everything else. Perhaps, sleep itself goes to slumber in their eyes....

My eyes rest on him. His manner I think changes. I don't know why and what. He isn't the one I seem to be familiar with. "*Arre*! Sivaram is here! Have you some *jilepis* left over? Or have you, the *Bhairavas* you are, devoured them?" he shouts. The pitch startles me. I thought his voice as gentle, as soft, as subdued, meant for your ears only.

I suddenly seem to have lost my bearings. That shout pulls me by the ears. When and where did I hear it? I'm sure I heard it before. Like lead poured into the ears, it settles solidly in there. But where? That ear-splitting voice of the Mother you can not erase ever. It echoes down the corridors of *Kala,* rousing the rabble from sleep but lulling them, again, by the very deafening noise.

The eyes snap a photo. I recall: that man with fiery eyes, drunk with pride, with the beads of skulls round his neck, with *vibhuti* daubed on the face thickly and a vermilion mark in the middle of the brows, strides as if he owns this side of the Ganga; as if the temple and *Bhavatarini* are his handmaids. Confidence-looking arrogance marks his every move. A look at him and people run helter-skelter. I quail and rush to a corner like an ant fearing extinction. "*Arre!* Where is that kid who calls himself Kali's child! Ask him to come here! Kali's child? My foot! With me around how dare he take the name of the Mother?"

Who is there to listen? But the Mother has always her ears to the ground. She knows when to draw the sword and when to take out the garland from her neck. A soft smile plays on her red lips, red with savouring the betel leaves, red with the blood, too, which for her, is no different from the juice of the betel leaves! Her eyes-unusually bright as if scenting a prey, blaze with thirst. Thirst that can quench itself only by devouring the demons of pride, the *pasu* that bristles with its might and wants to snap the rope to which it is tied.

The earth seems to wait in expectant dread. "Go forth child! Take my name and take my voice. Here! take them and face him!" He emerges from the room. Strangely no one inside there seems to hear or notice his slipping away from the room. He walks as if he is a sleep-walker-as if he knows every inch of the ground he treads on even when blind. ("As if?" what else can one do with words?) Every step he takes makes everything tremble: the earth that receives his touch has horripilations all over her body. Obviously, he is now *roudra,* the fiery, fearful one.

My dread disappears like a line drawn on water. I look expectantly for the unfolding—should I say, battle. "Where is that

Kali's child? Is he afraid? I know he should be with me around!
This is not deceiving those deluded kids hanging around him! Let
him come out from hiding. You will know what taking Kali's
name is!"

I get keyed up for a fierce encounter. I imagine all sorts of
things: that Kali's this child will take out a weapon—materialise
it, in fact—and uttering a *mantra* throw it at him and slay him.
Something like, I imagine, the slaying of the buffalo-demon. All
kinds of images flash through the mind. Stories heard, sagas read;
myths mouthful, miracles galore.

"*Ma! Ma! Ma!*" gently the chant forms on those lips. Almost
inaudible, the *ekakshara*—the one word gathers unto itself all the
matrikas. All the seed words that the mother loves are down the
tunnels of time, for ages chant and recharge themselves, renew
themselves like the *mantra* being chanted now: "*Ma! Ma, Ma!*"
Like the ocean swelling uncontrollably on the full moon day to,
reach out to the skies and touch it... the magical words gather the
combined strength of all the *aksharas* that escape the human lips
in adoration of that Radiant Being, the Mother.

The child is now in the middle of the courtyard. Exactly
behind him is the mother with a mischievous twinkle barely
visible on her lips. Before him is the swelling figure bursting at the
seams with anger; anger that he hardly understands himself! But
see, see quickly! The tone of the chanting has changed: the "Ma"
remains but the mood is transformed. Gathering momentum, they
are now sounds that shatter the ears, even the earth itself—renting
open its low-lying layers of consciousness lulled to sleep for ages.

The spine is tingling: an ant-like movement marks it. The skin
resists at first: as if to squash the ant. But it cannot be located. It
moves as if the body, the mind, everything belongs to it and
apparently I have nothing to do with what I think I am. "you are a
kid but a retarded one! I know what is good for you! Allow me to
move, get out! And watch!" the words merge with the movement
of the ant.

I watch: thunder rents the sky. "*Ma! Ma! Ma!*" it reverberates;
the trees sway in agony afraid they will get wrenched from their

roots. The birds circle in the *Ma*-rent sky; they sing in abandon; too many beaks, so many songs! All chanting to the rhythm of the Child's "*Ma! Ma! Ma!*" All sounds merge in the *Ma*. The creatures crawling on the earth. "Crawling?" wrong word. Dancing is the word. There are no creatures to crawl; there are only sparks that sparkle with light, light of varied hues, varied shapes. All coming forth and going into that *anahata* that is *anadi* and *anata:* "*Ma! Ma! Ma!*"

Eyes dot my entire body. I do not have enough of them to see what is happening before them. Like lecherous Indra getting *lingas* all over the body, I get eyes all over the *prema deha*. No space is left for anything else. Eyes transposed into the words, "*Ma! Ma! Ma!*" Words lose their opaqueness; they get sight, every word a window, all windows opening on to that window— that Gavaksha-that opens itself on, further on, to the Child in the courtyard. Chanting that seems endless, chanting that seems beginningless because all beginnings trace their beginnings to that beginningless beginning.

All eyes rivet to the centre of that courtyard. Courtyard? "See again, dear:" a gentle reminding. Oh my! How could this amnesia overtake me! How could I fail to see through?

The courtyard is transfigured: the *soundarya lahari,* wavelets of bliss, congeal into the Sri Chakra. It is the Mother's playing Ground, her *lila kshetra,* her very breath breathes life into that. The inert-*mrinmaya*-courtyard transfigures itself into the chinmaya Sri Chakra. Consciousness restored, awareness awakens; the ant settles in.

The angry ascetic
Lies prostrate before
The Child of the Mother;
Eyes closed in adoration,
All anger evaporates;
The *pasu* is Pasupati now!
Lying naked on the ground,
Inert but invigorated,
Lost in what visions
I dare not tell,

I dare not see
Even in vision!
The child, now the Mother,
Is dancing on the
Dead body in dreadful
Ecstasy; with eyes
Rolling, with tongue lolling
She strides across the
Body!
A glow gathers on the
White-the purest white-
Face of the Lord of the Animals.
The mother whispers with
Love-laden lips and lids
Half-closed in bashfulness, in sheer languor;
"Dance for me! Your
dance of destruction!
So that I can receive your seeds
And create again!"

"*Arre Baba*! Give that *jilepi* to him, to that kid over there; dreaming about what, I hardly know! Wake him up; he is a bit older. He constantly slips into sleep!"

The laughter that fills the room gently touches me. They all look at me, strangely. He, too, looks at me with a mischievous warning in the eyes: "keep everything in trust: what you see, what you hear! There is time for telling! Come, eat the *jilepi:* let me feed you!"

Has the tongue tasted anything sweeter? But is he again up to a trick? Where is the *jilepi*? Isn't it a huge crystal of sugar candy, gloriously white, white as Siva's body itself?

11

THE LOVE COIN

"Can't you come wherever I take you without being curious?"

I feel abashed. Yes, I am curious. Curious about many things. His bizarre behaviour often startles me. "Learn not to get startled by anything," he tells me. "Anything is possible." Why does he appear to hide himself? "There is nothing that I am that you are not," is his refrain. Can one believe it? But then, can one disbelieve it, either. He is never known to have told an untruth.

This time he puts four of us into a car. And he drives it himself. That is a revelation. I couldn't imagine him on the driver's seat. "Why not? You think I did not drive earlier?" he turns round and stares in my face. I sit sandwiched between two other friends. "My size is ideal for a sandwich," I often tell myself. Between the past and the present, between Ayodhya and Vrindavan, between Calcutta and Kamarpukur, between Parnasala/Panchavati and Dakshineswar Panchavati.... Imagination grapples with the enormity of the endless continuity, the enactment without end....

He stops eating much; he takes almost nothing. The procession of vehicles is a pageant of time that flows ceaseless, that fills the oceans, the sky, the earth, yea, the vishwa itself. Where are all these hurtling along, in vehicles of all shapes and sizes? They honk their horns for him to give way. He does, but not always. Is there a pattern even in that? "Some are hustled through, some lounge long, and long... weeds that grow and grow again and again!"

Who can make out the metaphor? Specially from one who is manifestly fond of play? Playing on words, he plagues those who are unaware! The vehicle grinds to a sudden halt. I lurch forward, groggy for a minute. Some accident; fatal, I learn. Nearly twenty to twenty five—quite a few children—lie bleeding from blood that is still warm, blood that takes time to congeal.

"You are good at metaphor. But have you touched their warm blood while alive? Then you will know..." he asks. The others in the car stare through the windows—are we supposed to get off and see what is happening? We hardly know. He sits immobile with those bifocals. Why doesn't he get off and see and, least, sympathise with those lying mauled, mutilated? Tender lives throttled, twisted, like marionettes pulled down after the show is over.

"They put my father in the mound they dug for him. Only one thought like the *dhruva nakshtra* hung in me: one day I shall be in there, in that place, thoughtfully kept vacant for me.... That is the only space where all space rushes to occupy its re-allotted, endlessly re-allotted seat. And my son does what my father got done. For his father he did the same. The exhilarating truth extinguishes tears. The eyes are dry: *dagdha beeja,* they dare not sprout!" An exultant chuckle kept controlled so far escapes him.

We rarely hear him speak with nostalgia. The words chase each other to get hooked on his tongue. We find him bursting with joy.... "If only the living know the dead, there would be a stampede by the living to displace the dead!" As usual he is cryptic, sly, locating something in a minute, dislocating it in another. "Did I tell you...." We crane our necks to hear. "How I am intoxicated by the fragrance that fills the air like the smell of sandalwood," he pauses with eyes far away.... We are filled with freedom from the dread of death that stares us from the roadside. "The fragrance floats from the burial ground right across my place!" Beyond all shock, we sit frozen. "Fragrance from funerals!" Whoever heard of that? If you don't hear does it mean it doesn't exist?

"It's cleared! Let's go!" he announces. We jump forward. He overtakes this time with gay abandon—every vehicle on the road gives way. The speed is beyond endurance. I feel frightened again. Does he want us to join that group lying on the roadside? Driving slowly so far and gathering incredible speed now. Nightmares of falling off the vehicle crucify me.

"Every crucifixion is followed by resurrection," come his words, barely audible, in that vehicle roaring along with the speed of the chariots of gods. "I am taking you to a resurrection." I feel tempted to ask: "how many crucifixions we were through?" Should I ask? "That knowledge is possible but does it help you? Tell me how it helps you then I shall certainly resurrect your former crucifixions!" he says.

That was a trigger: a scene forms. Getting into the boat to reach Panchavati is the only thing I consciously recall. Looking at the flowing river unlocks waves of remembrance. The waves of the past engulf me. I begin sobbing, sobbing as if by the time I see the steeple of the Dakshineswar temple I will die and have to be thrown into the Ganga... for another resurrection. "Amar badi *kothai?* Where is your place?" Someone asks with concern, sensing that I am far from "my" place. Can I tell him that I am coming home to my lover? Will he believe? "*Amar badi* Panchavati/Dakshineswar....." I murmur. He looks at me strangely. Did I lose someone? Am I grieving over someone consigned to the river that holds in her depths, the dead and the dying? That seems to be what his suppressed, eye-sockets goggle at!

Entering the banks of the river itself I do not recall. Entering that small *baitakhkhana,* can I forget that? He sits there on the bed, as if this moment is all that held him within the confines of a body. Do I see him as I see the bed? Much more intensely, much more palpably; for, the luminous bird of enchantment applied collyrium to my eyes drawn from the dust of those blessed feet that trod heaven and earth and beyond! He looks at me, serenity filling the sight. The body is glowing like molten gold; gold melted, moving away from its cupidity to lend colour to that *prema deha,* the love-body and in the process redeem itself from being condemned by him as *kanchana.*

"Come close, still closer!" the Presence coaxes. "I want to give you something." Hasn't he given enough! What more should he give, what more is left to give? Is there anything else up his sleeve, sifted through the sieve of time? Shored against the erosion of kala that Kali, like a granny, keeps in her magic box of eternity, shutting out mortality?

In a split second falls from his folded hands a love coin made of gleaming silver bearing the mark, the *mohar* of Kali, the Supreme Maharani to whom all other *ranis* have to pay ransom! I feel its presence in my hand as he places it there with those delicate fingers which play on the flute of time, the *nada* of all *nadaans* over vast stretches of time. Even as I look at the coin (mind you, it is a real coin, I can even show it to you if you so desire!), its solidity dissolves. Strange! It is transfigured: the stream-coin flows beyond the present, back to the past, forward to the future! An endlessly flowing river from the lovely locks of Siva with Parvati in the heart and Ganga on the head!

12

NO BANGLES ON THIS HAND...

"Dreaming?" I awaken. The reverse of the coin swings into view. The banks of the river bask in early morning radiance. I hardly notice when he changed seats. One among the four with us is in the driving seat. Enjoying his talk... anything on the road enchants him. Men and women slipping out of the hands of sleep and getting into the saddle of routine. "So many forms of the Mother, doing so many things: everywhere her hands, her eyes, her ears, her nostrils breathing through them all!" the words linger in the gentle breeze and lapse in silence.

This One is reticent, this time. Reticent to reveal. I guess he is lost in the wordless vision of *viratrupa*. Do you want to call it *samadhi*? An inadequate *sabda*. He does not seem to be sugar: he wants to taste sugar and transmit that relish, that *rasa* to everyone. (Are we ready to receive it?")

I see him relish the piece of mango, before he tasted it. Stubborn, I want to serve him myself. "Keep it there. I will take it," he says. When was this? I hardly care. I see the whole thing now. Am I not seeing her sitting before me now, like a child, playing a game that only children can play! Sitting in a chariot rushing along the river bank and now resting.

Again he says, "Leave the mango piece there. No need to place it yourself in my mouth." I am obstinate this time. "I must feed you with my hands," there is a tone of firmness in my voice. I hardly understand it: normally quiet, undemanding. Has he programmed this? Is there something he planned? "All right! But only one piece, mind you. Don't stuff me will all things like... Sabari!"

The river has ripples all over her body. The word strikes a
gong: irrepressible, indelible leaves of *smriti* rustle on the limbs of
the river; her waves saw endless panorama of the *lilas* of a
ceaseless procession of Paramahamsa on her banks. She remains
the vigilant eye of the unblinking, unwavering vision of the play
of the gods, their sport on the banks of her breast.

"I am waiting, dear. Where is the piece? I am hungry!" He
gets off the car and is really looking hungry. I am still inside the
car. In haste, I descend. Where are the others? I do not know. They
are just not there. The vehicle gleams in the rays of the rising sun.
Rays? Eyes, rather, eyes eager to witness this strange
stubbornness and its outcome. Why is this kid so petulant this
time? Do I know, myself?

Bending in adoration I put a piece in his mouth, now fully
open. I reel back! Hit in the face! Something I couldn't identify
hissed at me. That hissing sound sends a chill down my spine. It
seems it isn't there. The body itself seems to float and stretch itself
across the sky, the earth. Wherever the eye falls, there is her
radiant form! But the roving eye is transfixed, arrested in its
tracks. "Just look at me! Nothing else matters. Simply see! Let all
else cease!"

In a split second, the light of the sun dissolves, disappears. She
is the only One visible and in that awful mouth are moving
everything that the earth holds, the heaven dreams, the sky
perceives!

What did I ask for? You ask for things playfully! You do not
know what play is. "Don't you recall how a friend of mine reeled
back, paralysed with fear, perplexed with wonder, with all words
vanishing from the mouth! When he saw what you want to see?"
Am I not seeing, only just wanting to see? Then, how about those
mounds and mounds of food being devoured by that serpent inside
the mouth?

A smile gleams on her face: "Hear me! Let me myself give
you words to get at what you see! To penetrate through *sabda*
what is impenetrable." Words fall like petals from her lotus feet. I
collect them in the sanctuary of my heart: heart still shivering in
fright and fascination:

Manifold are thy forms
That have no beginning
No middle and no end;
I see thy two eyes:
The sun and the moon
-shrunk in size and seized by your eyes-
giving light that scorches,
love that redeems;
the burning fire is
extinguished by the
waters of the rivers and the seas!
Thy brows knitted in anger
Shake the worlds;
Thy third eye radiates
Warmth that is mysterious.
In thy jaws are masticated
Millions of beings;
In thy lap they fall, and
Nursed back to being
The endless saga of
Srishti, sthithi, laya
Sings the tunes of
Thy *Samaveda.*
Thy music lulls us into slumber;
Thy magic makes us witless
—until milk oozes from
 thy breasts and we
suck it with teeth
that inflict bruises!
In infinite compassion
Thou comfort us again
Taking away the bite from the teeth!
Can a human have eyes
Enough to see this
Thy form!
The twinkle of a smile, a

Star is enough to
Startle us!

"I know you will go back to Victorian syntax," his amused
voice wrenches me from the hissing serpent in the mouth back to
the banks of the river. My teeth chatter, the tongue is still hooked
to the roof of the mouth. Incoherence flays me. What I saw, what I
see refuses to fuse. "You know why I ask you not to make me open
my mouth?"

Slowly eyes return to sight! "Come! Let me touch you! You
seem to be not well at all!" He takes my hand into his. Why is he
wearing bangles? He is thrusting that hand into mine with gentle
force! No bangles on the other hand! Does he want me to go
crazy? Haven't I seen enough? Did I? Perhaps seen but not seen
through!

Bangle-seller! That was the first one who saw through him
while others just saw. Now a stream of memory surges through
me—transfusion of the blood of the past and the present makes the
sushumna erect. They mingle to efface the mist from the eyes.
"My mother, too makes bangles and sells them. In fact, they call
my family "the bangle ones," he speaks in a whisper. "But you
don't have bangles on both hands," like a kid I ask. "Since Mother
wears, Father does not: what the One does the Other need not!"

The river, alert to every syllable, flows freely now, heaving a
sigh of relief! That I have still my wits about. His grace. Otherwise
can a human taste the Reality very much? The bangle-seller is the
bangle-wearer! Both from beyond neither Bengal nor Andhra!
Radiant Sankhu Sri, the Conch bearers.

13

THE ONE WHO BIT INTO EVERYTHING

The other three appear. One is laughing in his sleeves. Perhaps, he knows him for a long time. They were, in fact, born, it seems within a few hours of each other! He is always the silent one. Tears gather in his eyes whenever and wherever he sees him. Like a shadow he follows him. (Of course, gods don't have shadows!) What tricks the Presence is up to, the silent one knows. Enchanting secrets must be lying in this one's bosom. Like a huge ship majestically moving in waters, carrying cargo that can hardly be seen... concealed from the curious gaze.

The other two stare at the vast expanse of water, as if they are seeing it for the first time. Perhaps, true. Seeing the river with him is vastly different from seeing it on your own. This is seeing through the secret passages. Secrets that time holds from all who opt to live and die in time. (Opt? I do not know. Maybe we don't have an option.) The effect is instant. One of them, an expert swimmer, jumps into the river as if an elusive lover beckons. With long strides he swims like a fish that is not thirsty in water. The fishermen looks enchanted, he, himself, swam in rivers of varied hues! Distant locales, divergent dialects!

Normally morose, the *drishya* makes me marvel too. "Dive deep, dive deep!" those eyes seem to exhort. For long you saved your face, swimming on the surface. Now is the time. Plunge headlong! Plunge with passion, with abandon. Nothing else matters. For once lose your face!"

The joyful fish

Swimming gloriously
In the river
Saying things to
Each other that
Only the river knows!
For knowing what
The river knows,
You have to know
Swimming.
Dare to dive to the
Bottom: the beloved
Is waiting to fold
You in her cool embrace.

What is this person's language? "Fish" and "beloved"?
Doesn't he know I can't bear the smell of fish, let alone eat it! And
"beloved?" Doesn't he know the Beloved is he!

Get into the water
Without getting wet!
Drink the water that
Turns into wine!
(if you know how!)
Dance on the waves
Of the river:
The waves, if you know how,
Congeal into the contours
Of the divine courtesan,
The beloved mother
Becomes the blissful lover!

What is he up to? Why is he filled with this madness when he
sees the river? Oh my! The hair on his body is bristling as if it is
tugged at the roots. The eyes themselves are aflame, a flush of
passion, red jumps into them. What visions pass through them,
who can ever know? Unless he tells. The body is swaying as if
unheard melodies are rousing the young one, the innocent one,
who has never known the passion-fruit....

The beloved cannot come
If you are bashful;

The mother, too,
—even the mother, too,
I shall say—never
Gives you a bride
Unless you ask!

He is raving mad! No doubt about it. I feel convinced I will be
insane before long. "You should become insane," he shouts with
glee. He has this disconcerting habit of knowing you inside out. I
recall what he said once, I thought, fun: "Every idea or thought
that escapes your mind or lips, I manage to catch in the net of my
attention."

None can escape
My net;
They think they
Do; escape from
My waters!
That they hardly know.
For me, too, there
Is no secret passage
To escape.
You bind me, too,
With the rope of
Your passion.

He drags me into the waters. Holds me with a grip that grips
through eternity. "Come, let's plunge into the river!" "I haven't
learnt swimming," I plead helplessly. "With me around none shall
drown." "But are you always around?" "Yes, if you really look
around and not just think that you are looking around!"

The ice cold waters
Fill the body with
The fire that only deep
Waters ignite!
And his grip tightens,
No letting go!
Arre! I know swimming!
Incredible! How like a

Whale I feel at home
In waters that wash
All dirt off the body!
With long strokes,
With eyes open,
In the depths of the river
I behold what I
Search for on earth:
Infinite forms of fish
Sporting madly in the
Deep! Sporting in
Sheer ecstasy,
Ecstasy that only
The fish let loose
From the noose know!

"You said you know no swimming!" he teases me. But where is he! I see no form that answers to what I could recognise on earth. This one I hardly know. The echo is familiar, the voice is friendly but there is no face that, I thought, I knew. He is like this always. Sly, sly beyond belief! But what lovable slyness!

The first to plunge into the water, I notice, is preparing to go up. Signal that all others should! Reluctant to enter then, I loath to leave the water now. Why can't I remain forever infolded here—the waves caressing the flesh so long stricken with life's fever! Dive and never surface, plunge in and stay, joyously surrendering to the waves. Go wherever they take you!

"Enough! Come up!" they shout—as if I am going to miss something unique, something that falls in your lap only after so many lifetimes. You may have to wait long, for such a thing to come before you. Not in dream but in flesh and blood. I hear so much in their shout.

A woman! Parched skin, sunken eyes, hair that is timelessly gray, gone gray even before it was black. With a pot held in her hands, this time. I see that she isn't even walking, she is floating like a phantasm—a phantasm of the living. Faltering steps, unsteady, imbalanced. She has eyes only for one as she comes down the steps of the ancient river. And that One doesn't need to look at her for hasn't he seen her long ago? She looks like a creeper that grows beside the river. Drawing sustenance, over the centuries, waiting for this moment again!

The one still in the water fills her pot. (Did she come for water, she got all the water she needs for aeons!) She doesn't look at anyone, even the One. She ascends the steps slowly as if she lost her eyes in his! And disappears in the corner.

"The one who bit into everything before he allowed him to bite into them!" The silent one whispers in my ears. Are we beside Godavari or Ganga?

14

THE BRIDE IN THE SALAGRAMA

Words spontaneously rise:
    Thou art
    The three *kutas,*
    Vagbhava, sound-source
    Kamaraja, the primal desire
    Shakti, the world as power.
    Thou art the darling child
    The *bala;*
    Thou art the counsellor,
    The *mantrini;*
    Thou art the commander
    The *dandanatha.*
    Effulgent, eternal
    Self-luminous, thy
    Prakasa craves to
    Become *vimarsa,*
    Then *spanda*
    Issues into *nada*
    Nada into *bindu*
    And your
    Art of Cosmic Love,
    Thy noose and nose,
    Is the *kama kala*
    That impels the
    Universe into being!

"Oh, you are fond of all that?" she chuckles in seeming amusement. But I could see love dancing in her eyes. "How movingly, deeply, abidingly those words enchant me," she says with the eyes what she denies with the lips. There is a gloss in the eyes that I see but rarely, no glass is glassy enough to cover that glow! Pleased at a precocious child showing off to bask in the affection of its mother. Casual, nonchalant, she asks, "Don't you remember that one... *Parasivavikarnikare*...."

See how mischievous she is! Her noose is really her nose. She can smell people: her *nasika* is the fatal seductress, the fragrance pulls, that fragrance pierces, that fragrance is the fragrance of earth and heaven, the divine and the human lock up in embrace, the Siva-Sakti-Sangama. "I am waiting to hear it from your lips!" she repeats.

Parasiva, the
Pure effulgent being,
Is reflected on
The mass of the
Rays of the sun;
The Mahabindu
On the *citta*-wall,
Appears reflected
In the pure
Mirror of thy
Creativity.

"Oh my! Though you got mixed up, you are right. Though you are not clear!" she teases and taunts, as usual. Once bitten, twice silent, I remain dumb without falling into the trap. She, I know, is the Great Trap, the *Mahamaya* that catches the unwary. The big ones get caught, the small ones are too small to be caught.

Silence reigns all around, there is a lull in the air. As if waiting for something momentous to happen. She, too, stretches herself in expectation, tense yet tension bereft of any anxiety. Only a sense of utter fulfillment, of absence of anticipation, that what is going to happen is going to happen. With just a movement of her eyelashes she directs my *drishti*.

At first, I do not see him. The mass of vegetation makes vision dissipated. I gather my diffused sight and look again. The Foggy One, Dhumavati, showers her grace: the fog lifts. Now I see him clearly. Strange, the sheer sheen of even his body is shielded by the Mother! I recall once he prayed to her: "Take back into yourself the gleam and the gloss and the glow; take the pillow-case, let me keep the soft cotton!" But, perhaps, the mother didn't fully agree: "Let my other children see the *soundarya* of this *bala,* my special daughter!"

That residue of radiance makes recognition rush into the eyes, like water long dammed up and released races along to fill every crevice of the earth. I never before saw him so youthful. Supple like a bent, unbreakable bamboo (he takes the bamboo pole on his shoulders and roams all over. Quite often, I see it even now!) that three-folds-navel-in-the-centre middle; the chest red with the colour of blood constantly rushing there, rushing as if it is bent on wrecking it. And those surprisingly full breasts (fool! they whisper: I have to store milk for countless children who come thirsting for it to suck at them again and again and again!) And the countenance?

Countless words
That rushed through
Your head and
Reached consummation
In the lap of that
Entrancing figure!
Countless words that
Filled the emptiness
Of your pen and made
It dance with delight
On the pages of your
Heart!
They are no count
When you come to count
The comeliness of
Those features that
Elude your pen, ink

And paper.

I struggle for words while all along words from other lovers
rush into my head:
Your slender waist
Girdled with jingling mini-bells:
Your body bent
Ever so slightly (lightly, too!)
By the weight of the
Breasts that bulge,
As if the frontal globes
Of the forehead of a
Young elephant are
Grafted there;
The face flouts
Before me: an
Autumnal moon!

But I want to repossess him myself (so my words count, don't
they?) "Enough," she hisses. Quiet and watch.

I watch. I know not from where. A radiant woman emerges
through the mists. Oh my! That description matches her every
inch. Perhaps we see her and write, both at the same time, seeing
and writing. Or, she shot at the words, splintered them, made them
disappear and in that emptiness entered and stayed forever. That is
what I see.

She beckons to him, already bent in adoration. A bewitching
smile crosses her lips, smile that transfixes humans, fixes demons!
Smile that makes the *sushumna* sing in wild frenzy! And is his
smile less! Hesitant at first, he approaches, his smile never
slipping in fright. Kali's this child has nothing to fear. He draws
her noose and pulls it up and down inside his nose. The nose
responds in rhythms of the primal breath that breathes through
every breath and breathes on after every other breath is lost in her
premalaya. His breath is even but passion-filled. He is
Chinnamasta, the current that courses in him. The current of
energy and power that flows forcefully, dissolving every thing on,
and in, the way. He grows enormous in size. He is muttering
something. I strain my ears to hear.

Strain? How foolish can I be? Why strain? Haven't I heard in
the depths of my ears the sound of the dancing *damaru*? The sound
that like a bride sleeps in the *salagrama* and instantly comes
awake with his magic touch, the touch that melts stones into music
and music congeal into stones, waiting for his *sparsha* for
spandana again! Thus, I now both hear and listen with ease and
catch his words:

No need to beckon
To me, dear!
To come and sit
In your lap.
I have taken
Away your fangs!
See! No poison
Affects me,
For, this time, I
Shall devour everything
In the blazing fire
Of my *tyagagni*
Fire that does not burn
But brightens;
Fire that does not singe
But sings; that is my fire
Your wiles have
No fuel left!
To fan your fangs.

She is now basking in the glory of this child who defies her.
Distance collapses, time is frozen. Her mask is ripped open.
Bewitching beauty becomes bounding grace; grace that undresses
a man and lifts that naked child into her lap. An entrancing
transposition that breathes love into my loins. Erect but no
penetration. Penetration but no consummation. The skull that
Chinnamasta wrenches from her body and drinks blood from is
now a temple that lodges firmly the mother and the child. I gasp,
breathless but with that

Breathlessness
That needs
No breath
To breathe!

15
"TEACH ME ENGLISH!"

"I want you to teach me," he announces with a glint in the eye (already shielded by glasses.) And, adds, "Teach me English."

Do I hear that right? Teach him? Me? And English, at that. Is there no limit even to *lila*? And should I have my face painted with the make-up of a guru, late in time, don the robes of *kashaya* and get on to the stage? And teach him, of all things, "all the world is a stage" and all that?

I feel like an "extra" in the play business, caught at the last minute roaming on the road for casting. Since the original has been lost in and to time. Is this his scenario? Should I now put on a beard too, dress in bark while my parchment tongue licks itself into the shape of words (and English, mind you.) ?

"You may not have much trouble. Earlier I learnt a few words of English. You know.... I plunged into the lap of the mother and cared for nothing then. Since many English ones come now I need to know English. Teach me."

"I do not believe it!" I nearly snap (after that snapping is there forgiveness?)

"So what? You didn't, of course, believe many things. This is one amongst them."

He is right. (He is, by the way, always, in all ways, right.) Do I believe when he tells me that we met earlier? That I saw him earlier? In many forms, with many faces? How he strains himself to make me believe, even now? That I see HIM alone? (often alone, too).

can I rightly deliver the lines? Do I have the right accent for a
wrong language (wrong: because it is not mother's tongue, I think,
foolishly). Of course, I commit the cardinal sin of disbelief: can he
learn well? Can he write and speak a language I myself feel out of
depth with?

A smile spreads across his face again. "I shall be obedient, sit
in front but remain unanimously anonymous. Even you will not,
often find me recognisable. Often I grow a beard. Your class, of
course, I shall come without one! Even then I'm the odd one
among so many even ones. You may not know me though you see
me."

When he gets into this mood no one can stop him. (No one
wants to stop him, that is.) Why does he talk like that? Does he
mean all that? How much of this is play and how much is *satya*?
He, of course, makes you believe this is it. Yet doubt plagues you
(as doubts always do, he says.)

Reluctantly, I agree. Do everything expected of me. He is, to
my unpardonable surprise, really good. Alert he sits, attentively
he hears. But with glasses always on. I am curt and business-like.
Deliver my lines, take money. (But, of course, I deliver my lines
with passion: he sits passionless, *achala,* appears satisfied.) The
course is over.

"Now that all that is over, I want to give you *dakshina*," he
says. The producer pays me. No need for that from you. But he is
firm. "Let us go, take a bath in that river; rather you take it; I
already had one. I shall then pay you." Why displease him. I dip
my head into the river that flows from the gaze of Saraswati, the
Goddess of Learning.

I emerge from the waters, "I am not I"—I realise. Where is
he? On the banks, waiting, as he always does, did and will, with
clothes for me as his *chela*! Can anything be more blessed? The
tormentor becoming a *chela,* and the former *chela* now a mentor!
And he has grown a real beard, now!

16
THE CAT OR THE MONKEY

"What do you want to be, a cat or a monkey?" he asks. The serene face does not betray any frivolity. It appears serious and intent on knowing. I am wary. Almost to the point of laughing. Surely a joke. Even if I am reborn (which I think is certain; no "if" about it!) he would not make me enter the body of either of these two. The one feline and the other *chanchala,* always jumping about restless. Hardly anything to choose between.

He sits looking content at the landscape. No other words he speaks. The place is not familiar to me. I do not seem to have visited such a place before. At least not as far as active memory can recall. But then, should one know?

I never seem to have enough of looking at that face. All those lines, "the face that launches a thousand ships" seems to me so much chaff. (Not chaff exactly, but grains that have no vitality left in them.) This face you can't see with the eyes, but unless you see it you won't know. I know, I sound mad. Yes, I am mad. Only madness makes you see that face. Mad, mad, mad.... I feel like rolling the word round my tongue. Unhinge the normal, you will get this abnormal, this supernormal.

Have you at any time seen—I mean really seen—the face of a child smiling in its sleep, lying, it knows, securely in the lap of the mother? Her lap is the cradle that she rocks gently and from that rocking she rules the world. Lulls you to sleep, breaks the sleep, launches you into life and after its sanity is over, calls you back to the cradle's madness. And whenever we smile (smile and not smirk or snigger) we smile only because we are lolling in that lap in langour. That child's smile is similar this child's smile. Since a smile is a smile, he is always asleep! That lights up the face.

Have you seen the lovers of any brand? (any brand, mind you) looking at each other and smiling? Smile which does not appear on the face but suffuses it with the warmth that floods the eyes. Nothing visible but nothing concealed either. Across vast distances the concealed is revealed for each other and the revealed is concealed for others. That is this man's face. One simply floats in the pranic energy of that countenance. It is virile without any vulgarity about its virility. It is feminine to its core without being effiminate. It is manly but not in a macho way. No hero but a zero and yet Number One is with him: he puts it before all the zeros.

I hardly know how he manages to look, what do they say? so "hep"! Notice that elegantly trimmed beard. A hippie gone haywire can fall for it. Of course, *purohits* are notoriously unkempt—only once a month they shave off. But this one sports a beard not grow one. Who knows how much of magic lies hidden in the roots of that lush hair! Perhaps, the magic is to hide his identity; hair is his hide-out. Remove it and with a shudder you see Sri Ram, Sri Krishna. In fact, any One behind the Many! "I want it this way," he seems to say. "Let me hide and seek!" behind the beard.

"Stop seeing and see through," he gently admonishes. "I am a *gavaksha,* the window, the eye of the celestial cow, the Kamadhenu. Open the window on to anything you want to see and I ensure, you shall see that which you desire." I can hardly take my eyes off his face and gaze at the eyes. "No need for you to do that. Just relax and allow me...."

That does it. I see now. The courtyard crowded with people. They appear devout but waiting, in fact, for the daily dole from the Mother's *bhandara,* chatting, gossiping and sniggering; and they have only one butt of their ridicule: the young priest. What has he not done to desecrate the *Bhavatarini*! What cheek he has! He puts food into her mouth one minute and the next he takes it off from her mouth. "You want me to eat, first, Ma! All right!" and

swallows it. He puts his hand under her nostrils to feel her breath!
What antics! He is mad, raving mad. We would have turned him
out but then the equally mad Mother is fond of him.

There is a commotion. They crane their necks to see what is
happening. Has the doling out started? Then they must rush. But I
can see no doling. Instead the young mad *purohit* enters the vision.
He is doing a strange thing. Strange even for this stranger. Where
he caught her I can not see: a cat is resting in his lap; a cute, fluffy
white one. Dazzlingly white, not a speck of dirt or dust anywhere
on her body. Oh, my! What eyes! Two crystals glowing in the
white face. Eyes that strangely remind you of those I see in... just
let me recall.

Yes, those eyes are familiar, even with eyes folded, one can
uncannily re-member why not? All eyes, all over, are her eyes.
She lends them, her bank of eyes is always full. Not just eyes alone
but sight. She can give eyes but withhold seeing; she can withhold
eyes and yet allow seeing. It is all her whim and fancy. The kitten,
I notice, seems to have got her own eyes straight into her sockets!

My madness now becomes a frenzy. I become nearly insane,
insane with impatience. What is this man up to? Is he going to
strangle her as food for the All-devouring One? Is he going to
throttle it in moments of his known madness? Nothing like that
happens, however. He takes into his hand an earthen cup resting
on the ground. Clean, gleaming, as if the mud that moulded the
cup is something magical, something like the paste that the
Mother rubbed off on her oily body and licked into the shape of
the Lord of Obstacles!

The little one mews helplessly. There is nothing that she can
do until S/he comes to feed her. She is used to surrendering to the
moods of the Mother. Doesn't She know when the young one is
hungry? When the little one has to be lovingly fed? Should the
little one even mew? She has ears and eyes everywhere. All that
she has to do is to surrender—render unto her everything!

He puts her on the ground and places the cup before her. In
adoration he prays with hands folded. See how the kitten is
accepting that as if it is her due, as if it is the most natural, the most
normal thing to do.

The group gathers round them. Distanced from all criticism, dislodged from all hostility, they watch the spectacle with intensity that matches his ardent devotion. The mother disrobes them of their distempers. They are disembodied beings watching something that only the lucky can see!

The little one is lapping up the milk; as if it is starved for long. Starved for this moment for a long, long time: a magical moment when the child feeds the mother, the kitten feeds the mother-cat! Roles are reversed, the child becomes the mother; the mother becomes the child. The kitten becomes the mother, the lover feeds her in fondness. Both the eyes of both are in the love—eye that ravish me.

A smile gathers on the face of the crowd. First someone ventures to laugh a bit loud. The intensity breaks. The spirit is caught. They join the fun. They are literally roaring with laughter until tears of joy at their luck drop from their eyes. Oh! How they laugh! The priest looks around and the little one too follows suit. They join the crowd.

Oh, *Ma*! How many games you play! How many pranks both of you play together! Is there any end to them? Aren't you both mischievous beyond measure? You dissolve the many and playfully become One. You get tired soon. You cannot, I suppose, remain for long as One. The *kama kala* stirs in your breast, in your sleep. There is no fun in being One for long. "I must become the Many." The *Brahmayoni* has to throw out from her womb, many, many and many more. In fact, countless beings that get created out of the sheer joy of emptying the womb. Then the play begins all over; the kittens mew in surrender. The monkeys jump about as if they own the womb!

Sleep overpowers me. I drift into it with welcoming arms. I sleep light, for who can sleep heavy when that Light lightens your sleep! But I do sleep. Time and space dissolve. I even snore. Snore with abandon, with joy that I saw the kitten that mews and the mother that rushes to feed it. "What a vision!" I say to myself even when I snore. Can one see such things except with mother's grace when she daubs your eyes with the anjana of her infinite love.

But someone is shaking me by the shoulders. "*Arre baba* how heavily you sleep! Can't even this wake you up?" Grudgingly eyes come back to sight. I am startled, feeling groggy. "Can't you see this kitten is mewing at your folded feet! For so long. We thought you both were playing a game: that too at this late hour."

Eyes refuse to believe what they see. A live cat is at my feet. This is a grown-up one. No longer a kitten. It is a cat and it is for real. I clutch at the sheets on the bed. They are real. I can feel them, really touch them. Everything in the room is familiar to me now.

Even the cat. I lift it into my arms. Look into her eyes: slyness is writ large in them. "You saw me in vision; you see me for real. Now, now is here now, forever. Is there anything that I can't show you, once you settle in where I place you; once you know you can't settle in anywhere except in my lap!"

A mad, mad frenzy of laughter engulfs me. I love that laughter and surrender to it.

17

NITYA AND NATAKA

She is the play; he is the play within the play. How many scenes he enacts and in how many scenes he forgets the enactment! Strange, he remembers the Mother, but disregards her play and plunges into the play inside the play.

Sounds incoherent? Yes, it is. If you saw what he makes me see. Every time I see him he reminds me of one who willingly cancels, deletes whatever he has to do. And reveals, instead, something unexpected. Unpredictable, that is the thing. You expected to see him; instead you see her actually; he turns round and says and shows all that is, his play.

You must be prepared for strange things. I forget that; and I get caught. Caught napping, snoring, sleeping. And often dreaming. All these are made to move away in a minute. You end up envisioning what you thought as the beginning of re-visioning. He and she seem bent on confusing you: when this feeling seems to settle as a conviction in the mind, the mind itself is made to do a vanishing trick. Effortlessly there is fusion.

Often you think he will come home and eat. Not "eat" exactly. Take whatever we are privileged to offer him. But that does not happen that way. He announces his coming when you least expect. Things are, he says, pre-designed. Expectations are outside, are nonexistent; only the pre-designed is. "Rough hew them what you will," there is only design that decides, the shapes, literally everything, from the fall of the sparrow to the largest accident on a bridge when the vehicle plunges into the water and offers an instant passage to death.

Death! That unlocks what I am made to see. What an experience! Rare to get the director himself donning the role of the hero. Moreover of the Lord of the Cemetery. Rare when *nitya* and *lila* dance in paradoxes that leave you groggy! Groggy? No. Gasping for sanity, running to clutch the nearest straw. And the straw turns out to be a serpent that hisses. And makes you come awake where you were asleep.

Could I otherwise see this thing beginning as an episode in a play and jumping from the play into my lap and become a live, seen reality. *Bhavamukha,* he says. The threshold of consciousness. You plunge into it. The threshold recedes and you see that, from the beginning in the very nature of things, all thresholds are lines drawn with a stick in *akhanda chaitanya sagara.* The shoreless ocean of consciousness. Do you get what he teaches me? That the players can leave the stage and mingle with the audience. Absurd? Of course, what is his *maya*? Radiant play, recurrent play, relished, relishable, renewed, renewable, known and knowable-play of his consort, Maya! The ageless absurd One.

Or else is it possible to make sense of this? The play is to begin. Sivaratri. Auspicious for him. He is that himself. How do we know this unless he condescends to reveal it? The one who is to play the role is sick. He can't come. Sickness designed deliberately. They try desperately for someone to take his place. Cancelling the performance is ruled out. They just can't do that; they have to keep awake: *jagarana,* through the night. Only a *pasu* will sleep on the night of the Lord of Animals, Pasupati. But then what is to be done?

Like everyone else he looks forward to seeing Siva, on the stage. That which doesn't age is the stage. Siva is ageless so is the sanctity of the *rangasthala.* His face is already indrawn. The mood seems to be descending. Serenity settling on the sedate visage. Inherently detached, he is now increasingly so. His long locks, slightly matted, his eyebrows knitted in the middle show the imperceptible third eye.

One among the agitated in the crowd: his eyes fall on him. They suddenly light up. Searching for Siva when he is right in their midst; the child in the cradle and you look for her everywhere else! He is reluctant, reticent, in fact. Who would willingly part with the secrets behind the stage? All cannot be invited to see before footlights what is there backstage. The gods return but they don't turn out their mysteries into scenes before everyone. "But then those who see may not necessarily know. May not be able to detect: the difference between the original and the copy." He muses thus and agrees.

Smeared with ashes,
The one who
Reduces everything
To ashes ascends
The altar-stage.
Matted locks hold
The Ganga; the
Serpent coiled round the
Neck is glistening,
Heaving and hissing;
The throat that holds
The poison that lost all its fangs is
conch-like; it is
the great being
and non-being.
The poison is and is not.
Firmly planted on earth
His feet fondly
Cherish memories of
The Dance of Dissolution,
The *Prayalayanritya,*
They wait willingly
Patiently for the
Dance to begin again.

A hush envelops the audience. Their eyes lose their sight. Instead, they are given bifocals that see and not see, too. For some the vision is unified. For others, it is something that they do not understand, but they do not try to, either. Some gasp for life: "This is Siva himself! The One not illusory, not a performer. The Real

One." In adoration they rise and in amazement they chant. Chant with that rhythm that only the Siva-possessed bring to their chanting. Vani herself enters their throat in honour of this live act.

The hush deepens. The rhythm and music intensify. Reach a crescendo

OM NAMAH SIVAYA
OM NAMAH SIVAYA
OM NAMAH SIVAYA

Siva listens, the already lighted-up visage is luminous! A blazing aura of renunciation, *tyaga,* suffuses his features. No one dare go near. They will be reduced to that which they are and think that they are not: the ash that is *vibhuti,* the *vibhuti* that envelops life with ash and death with splendour.

One among the many, I stay with them and sway with them. Consciousness slowly comes back. Still in a daze and with no prospect of the play continuing, they disperse. Murmurs are afloat: "There is something of a miracle in what happens. We do not know." I, too, do not know but have for the present at least— no wish to know. I am about to step out of the grounds. I look at him again. The last, lingering glance. I think, one for the road to Dakshineswar.

That moment he chooses to open his eyes. Beckons to me, "Stay back," the gesture of the Lord of Gestures seems to say. Did I see it right? Yes. He is beckoning.

I stay back. I never so far stayed back to meet anyone off or on a stage. Some reason he must have. The night advances the time all his *Bhairavas* bask in his effulgence. The time of night that the mother is awake while her children are asleep. Strange voices fall on my ears. The anklets on his feet? The drum in his raised hand?

No such thing. Is he the same Siva I saw on the stage? Perhaps, he discarded all the dresses that make for recognition. Does he need anonymity? "See, we meet again!" the discreet tone is back. His eyes disappear, instead glasses appear. I cannot see whether the eyes on the stage and off the stage are the same.

"Come closer," he says. Quite normal, not casual but not formal either. An unmistakable, unperceived aura.... I strain to see it; struggle to evoke it. Then I see....

A sight, ever so light, a tremor on the hand (the right hand?). Uncanny alertness can only make you guess it, let alone see it. Those strong hands with the strength that is supple and graceful. On my part I am (I can only say strangely) relaxed. Neither tense expectation nor moronic stupor.... Meditators have a word for it: "alert passivity"that sums up my mind (set?)

The face is now remarkably, radiantly relaxed. "Nothing that is unusual is going to happen," it seems to say. "If it appears like that, it only is a sense of wonder, *adbhuta,* a sense of *ascharya,* surprise, that ought to be our response to everything in nature. Look at this that way!"

Suddenly a *salagrama* shyly, but glowingly, as if it is still aching with the warmth of those hands emerges and, (delighted and not dazed at all, note) I receive it in my hands. From the hands of this Siva comes that precious product of the "river Gandaki!" as he says. From the *lila* of the stage to the *nitya* of my experience. What an odyssey, what a *prasthanam*! He catches me like a frog in the mouth of a king cobra. You can never come out. He has to swallow you to make you alive. All those wallowing in woe—the sorrow that sorrow is and is not—have to be swallowed by him.

Don't be lost in a reverie, he says without stating it. A dazzlingly white Nandi is staring now from his hands at the Siva-salagrama in my palm! "They say no *darshan* of Siva without Nandi saying so! So here take it!"

Armed with Nandi in my hands, this time I dare to see the ash-smeared One in the face. I do not blink; nothing is blurred. No cataract in the eye. Everything is crystal like in its transparent purity and clarity.

The *salagrama* and Siva break into laughter. Nandi is ecstatic; it is vigorously nodding its head. They *are with me even now.* Even you can see them. Would you like to?

18
SITA'S SMILE

"You do very strange things and those quite often. I can't make head or tail of it!" One of those rare moments when I can tell him my helplessness. And my annoyance born out of this helplessness. That he does things which are strange is known. But that he says things which are equally bizarre is not very much known. Saying, for him, I know, is seeing; and if he thinks fit, showing us. That is, making us see, too.

Do you think that I would otherwise see them all on my own, with my already myopic eyesight? Myopia is a wrong spelling; its actually spelling is *maya*. *Maya* and *manas* go together he often says. And their function is to measure out adequate doses of infatuation and misperception. So that we play the roles given to us without being conscious that this is a play and these are roles. And what delight he derives from this myopic "drama"! Clearly he does. No other word would otherwise explain the verse and the perverse in the play.

I sit quietly but the mind is not so quiet. I begin wondering why he makes me use words, form sentences which I know cannot even remain conscious of what shape things take. They begin in one way and end with where the beginning has no link. Word-based beginnings turn out to be envisioning endings.

"I can't make head or tail!" I say and pause. He listens and leaves it there. Let it lie there like the long, unending tail of Hanuman. Spreading itself across vast stretches of time: the tail I mean. "Catch the tail, you should get to the head!" he says cryptically, in so subdued a way that for "tail" you hear "fail" and for "head" you make out "dud". I am one! Or else, how could I fail to see what is there right before me. Unrolling itself: a saga of wonder, of great relish and rapture that you are meant to nourish in the depths of your being.

The tail need not always be that of a serpent. Serpent is not, perhaps, everyone's cup of *sadhana*. That requires you to be a *vira*, a real hero. Then only you can tame her head and tail. But the tail of a monkey is not that awesome. Relatively, "You think so! It is equally...." The words remain incomplete. Or, I find no need to hear further.

I see the inside of his room. I am back in that. I can't see anyone around. He sits as usual engrossed. A little lamp shines in a corner. Since all of us cannot see the light he is, we require our little lamps. (that is why temples are kept dark, or at least were so until not long ago. They are fully lighted now and darkness has intensified.) "Engrossed" I say. Entirely unconscious of the gross (*sthula*), that is what it means.

I am not sure he sees that I see him. A smile lights up his face. The candle sees its master's smile and, blushing, withdraws. The candle is snuffed out—grateful that it is saved the humiliation of throwing light to illumine the One whose effulgence effaces the two faces of light and darkness. Oh! How long he sits, like a rock! Immovable, impenetrable, totally impervious to everything outside. As if he is dead. Only the rhythms of breath register a form. The breath is drawn in the playground of the mother. This is felicity from which none need absent himself or herself for a while. You can breathe in felicity forever. And that rhythm radiates the face and the smile. At perfect ease.

But what happens now rattles me. He is not like that, as far as I hear and see. He slips into sound sleep. Or, rather since he is lying on the ground on his side, stretched full length on the back I think he is sleeping. On the contrary, I seem to sleep. For six years not a wink of sleep dare cross those eyes. Nidradevi is bidden a gentle good-bye. Until summoned again. I sleep, or else how can I imagine that he is sleeping?

Strange! Am I becoming a victim of hallucinations? I pinch my flesh in panic. No. I am still flesh and blood. Not a disembodied being. So far, so good. Then where does this *vanara* come from? How does he enter? I know the door is closed. It is nearly midnight. And I watch all along—with unblinking eyes. (Ever since I saw him [not the *vanara*] I see to it that sleep does not become a mote that troubles continuingly seeing!)

The *vanara* surely knows what is where in that room. Straight it hops but silently, stealthily (as if he is treading on soft silk!). And hops to the niche where he keeps fruits, a banana generally. Obviously, the monkey has ancestral claims on the fruit. It touches the feet of his Lord and Master and gulps it down.

Stung, he rises. I get the distinct sound of a button being switched as it were, on and energy courses through-suddenly. The body registers strange movements like the current in a live-wire jumping from one pole to another. Like the monkey jumping from one branch to another, releasing the urge to play, to commune, to indulge in *ramana kreeda*. The *spandana* is instant, spontaneous, invigorating.

See his strides! He has already crossed the courtyard. The feet do not seem recognisable. They do not touch the ground at all. I hardly keep pace. How fast he walks. The smile is brighter but he is totally unaware—seems so to me. He heads towards Parnashala-Panchavati. Where is the *vanara*?

Limping along I trail behind. He has no use for me, obviously. I get rattled. Has he written me off? He does not look back. He has eyes only—for what? Where is he heading with that stride that is quite unusual of him. He seems eager to meet someone he waited for, a long, long time. Waiting, in fact, endlessly for... and unmindful, I think of me trailing behind.

Surely, I am mad, this time. Time I thought I got to be checked by someone. Do I see a tail slowly, slowly, but perceptibly emerging again. Sure, it is there. I see it, as I see anything else-in the eye that measures to being an eye. He is swaying this way and that. I stare engrossed (rare moments need this en-gross.)

Oh, my! Not on him

Who else has
That smile,
The smile that
Captivates her
Lord and Master!
The smile that
Survives all sorrow,
Sorrow that is
The saga of her
Existence itself,
Sorrow that she
Bore in her bosom,
Until she withdrew
Herself into the
Bowels of the earth
Whence she came!
She is Sita of Ramachandra
The Janaki of Janaka,
The inhabitant
Of the habitat
—the boundless heart—
of Hanuman!
See how he smiles in recognition: and beckoning she
whispers!
Come, child.
I shall give
You the best
I can bestow:
My smile:
In anguish
It adorns you;
In ecstasy
It engulfs you;
In everything
That you do, it
Shall be with you,

The Eternally Exquisite
Smile that enchants
Everyone that looks
At you.
Over the stretch
of time, it comes
to you; across
centuries to come
it shall be the
reward of everyone
that loves this
Radiant Ramakrishna.
I now know
Why I fell
Forever, flat,
For that face!
Resisting that
Smile?
You try; it is
Like resisting
The waves of
The gentle river
That greets you
In grace, in
Warmth, in
Woe, in sorrow,
In disease and
Death;
The smile drips
Drops of *amrita:*
You need hardly
Any hardy *pranayama,*
To catch the drop.
Just be the cup, the conch
That catches
The Swati-rain.

I seem about to slip into the blessed oblivion that obliterates all that needs to be.

His laughter awakens me. He is back to his hilarity. In a mood to tease, to test, to transfer his love, in fact. Is there any special reason that he should laugh now? Of course, I am not that stupid. That smile is this laugh. I may not cognise. But can I not at least re-cognise? En-vision?

"I thought you thought that that was just an image lying on the ground in Panchavati-Parnasala!"

I feel like a boy-baboon caught stealing *jilepis* carefully hidden from his greedy eyes. But one glance at him and laughter engulfs me and I devour him! Like Vatapi! Let me be a monkey, too.

19
PATRAM, PUSHPAM, PHALAM, THOYAM

I remain immersed in the felt Presence. With the mind empty of distraction, with eyes that both register and register not. I just enjoy absence of all sensations of his Presence. Not that sensations cease; they are still very much there. But they cease enlisting "my" services. "I am," in the only sense those words ought to have; all other meanings you so cleverly attribute to them do not seem to be. Only one meaning exists: and that exists outside meaning and meaninglessness.

I am not sure I can convey what I feel. But it does not seem to have anything to do with such feelings. Let me put it this way: these are moments of my being that wait like an angler to catch the fish in the net; the snake-charmer to catch the serpent by the tail. Moments when you just are and since that seems to happen, you totally in tune.

The music is heard when such tuning is spontaneous; nothing forced about it. Surrender that is spontaneous, this is what it means. Surrender is the only eye that can see these (and in these) things. Surrender is rendering ourselves to the Presence without even being aware that we do so! Then miracles happen.

Miraculously natural. Naturally miraculous. You think I am playing on words, play on words so long as his play doesn't seem to begin. Begin, that is, for you. For it began ever since creation began, ever since he drew breath with the sheer joy of being. Sans breath he exists; for to start breathing is to start the drama of life. Once the drama begins, ending also begins.

That way begins this experience. Experience that moves from the heart's eye to the eye in the body. Both eyes complete the circle of experiences. Like the circle around the full moon on the day of *Pournami* with *chandra* (moon) as the *bindu,* the dot, the *chakra* (circle) forms itself. Seeing it is a rare event but rarer still is to see it with nature's eye. Nature's eye is the eye that does not need an eye to show herself. That is the way this experience comes through.

That man always sits in the back. Never obtrusive; shy, but drinking in every word that drops from his lips. Literally every word. And every word is a blazing unquestionable command for this man. To be obeyed as soon as spoken. To be followed the minute it is formulated. Doubt is unthinkable; for, he has no thinking to speak of since thinking drags doubt from its embryo-mind he gave up thinking ever since that Presence pierced through his *granthis,* the knots (if they ever exist) of his being.

That way this man heard the Presence saying "Can someone try to get me an *amalaki* fruit? I heard it is good for health and I want to try it." All of them nod their heads: some even say, "we shall try" (in God's own time, they mean). I, too, hear. I hear them much more than most. But then I know that this is not the season for that kind of fruit. Not even one you can get. I even think, "doesn't he know that? He doesn't, I am sure. But then he is strange and says things that every time I hear intrigue me."

Is he testing, teasing, or is nature so docile to him that she will ensure that he will get the fruit, at least one. (Since One implicitly accommodates and extends herself as the many, getting One is as good as enjoying the Many.) Even if it is out of season? Most think, some are even certain, that the *amalaki* cannot be there in that season. So they concentrate on what he teaches and bypass what he needs. They credit nature and not the Presence. So divisiveness—that he and nature are two separate things—aborts their attempt, to get the fruit, in the very beginning.

But not this man.... If "he" wants, Nature shall obey. That is the man's conviction. Nature jolly well make at least one *amalaki* available. Since he says he wants one. Nature is his *bhandara,* his storehouse. It better look around and give him one; find one for him. No word of his shall go without extension into truth. Thus the man begins the search. The search that taxes all his energy. That impoverishes his health. But he does not feel it that way—all his energy he pours into the hunt for the fruit that is rare.

What burning faith in the words, faith in the truth of the words, conviction that faith is nothing else but miracle. That it makes the seemingly impossible possible. Faith not only in things that are seemingly beyond what are.

In fact, I recall his doing things that even faith quails from doing. Once he heard the Master: "Doctors can hardly attain *mukti;* they are too pretentious. They assume they are Gods and fancy that their medicine can cure anything." Promptly the man takes his medicine chest and throws it into the Ganga. In a split second he consigns it to the river and the glow of carrying out his guru's words transfigures his face. "Glory be to the Guru" he cries in ecstasy.

And no wonder in a remote village-which combing the entire countryside he found—an *amalaki* tree does have an *amalaki,* a single one, like a jewel in the crown. He knows this will happen. He is overjoyed. His guru's word is law. And the word is *amalaki,* and the *amalaki* is there. Tenderly he plucks it from the tree, (grateful for its keeping one in tact!), folds it in his cloth. He rushes to Dakshineswar. But doesn't rush inside. Even with what he wants, triumphantly in his hands, he seems shy.

I savour that moment of utter unconcern for pushing forward, even when, it seems he has the right to do so. That is what he likes most. I see him surrounded by devotees. Talking to them at length on belief in the words of the guru. That the guru tests you as a goldsmith tests gold. Ruthlessly inexorable. When his words seem impossible to believe, that precisely is where faith blooms. Faith flourishes when belief takes wings and flies away, never to be seen again. For, belief's wings are clipped by faith! Faith drafts the wings to herself and takes off into the sky: it never gets grounded.

"I know you have something up your sleeve," he says to the man bashfully waiting. Those gathered look back. What could he bring, except a few pice worth of puffed rice! Don't they know! They do not, in fact, know. For, they refuse to believe, even when they know that nothing is unachievable for this one.

They gasp: where did he conjure this? An *amalaki*? Does he have some magic in him? Where did he go and how did he get this? See how tremulously, with tears brimming in his eyes he places that in his soft, tender hands! Can the eye register a rarer, more ravishing scene than this? The Master looks at his hands: the *amalaki* seems to him the brightest, the costliest of gifts that one could give. He looks at the doctor; that is, this *bishak* that cures *bhavaroga* looks at that *vaidya* who ceased to be doctor ever since this *bishak's* medicine began effecting a cure.

I watch my own eyes dance in ecstasy. Ecstasy that engulfs them: everyone there, everything there. Only he and the *amalaki*-locator surface in the waves of joy. And I see him tasting it with relish, with—shall I say—gusto? The one who found it is smacking his lips inwardly! If he eats, isn't it that everyone ate? Should anyone be left out?

I seem to do, to feel left out. All that is all right. For others. Not for me. I come late in the day. I really want to taste it. You can even call me greedy. Who says I am not? I want to be in the "shoes" of that *amalaki*-procurer. I want to feel that in my hand, that fruit, I mean. And now in the month of *Karthik* when it is specially precious.

I am jealous of those days. I am really racked with intolerable nostalgia. I want him to come palpably before me. And this time he should give me the fruit. Not I giving him. I have little energy left to search for it. Age seems to catch up with me. The Kali Age, I mean. Lilliputs of little faith and less love, but lots of impatience. At long-drawn rituals. Hectic pujas, Heroic mental gymnastics.

I get my Krishna through my colonial cousins. I smell my mother in and through my mentors from overseas. You can't blame me. Ever since he built the bridge we cross over. From one space to another. Things seem to change. *Kaliyuge annagatha prana,* he says. Age of Iron is the age of gluttony, of food-based foolishness. But how are we to be blamed? We didn't choose to come here on our own—this time of day and date.

Wild fantasies displace everything. No need for LSD. I have (seem to have?) a built-in drug: the powerful pill of all that is denied escaping into the safety-value of dreams and dazed fantasies. That way comes this crazy desire. The urge to taste the fruit of the bidden not the forbidden tree: the *amalaki* (I learn he is specially fond of this!)

How maddening can be this crazed curiosity, this dementing desire. Memories beyond certitude crucify me. Memories of moving with him, of listening to him, of seeing him singing, sharing, suffering.... Of seeing anything and soaring into *samadhi*! Of tasting anything and devouring the Mother! Of smelling anything and scenting her in everything that is smelt! Of touching anything, anyone and the touch-bell tolling him back to the tender breast of the Mother; of hearing anything and the "unheard" *anahata* unlocking itself-breaking all barriers, crumbling distances, collapsing all the contours of *maya* and plunge into her.

The spectacle reduces my glasses to rubble. Can I find their use again? Should I discard them going in for newly-powered ones? Have I become much more myoptic? Much more of the man of maya, of the *Mahamaya,* the Playful Paramour, par excellence?

I can't see anymore; anything any longer. I get into the river to drown myself, to drift into her waves with the delight of the child denuded of the desire even to swim and save himself. Utter abandonment unnerves this child. Un-nerving is exactly the thing. That done, the Primal Serpent plays joyfully, pierces the pores of the *dehalaya,* the temple-body. Everything is alive; the drooping, drowsy petals are erect! The spine gets its eyes, the body eyes.

He asks me to close the room. Bolt it from inside, bar it firmly. I am puzzled. Boundless space is his being. Then how can one draw the Lakshmana rekha, the line of *bhava* that fixes the *mukha,* the threshold? "I have my reasons, *baba,* close everything" he assures without articulation. "But keep the windows open!" he motions.

"Sit near!" I, the slave of strong thresholds, of frontiers, hesitate, for a second. Then the line drawn earlier disappears. The doors closed swing open; not to the corridors of time but into the vasts of timeless, space free spaces!

The moon shines exultantly in the sky. He is waxing with fresh vigour; some transfusion takes place. The clouds joyfully disappear. "Let our beloved shine in full glory and see the fun!" they whisper to each other and hide in the wings. Quiet reigns all over. A bath in the light of *chandra*—how bracing it is! I already have one in the heat of surya during the day. Surya and Chandra gently lead me—the widowed consciousness wending its way to the Beloved Mother! Breath comes and goes on its own; freed from the frame it designs its own rhythm. I re-sign my-self to that.

Tremors that I notice, but neglect to know what they are, begin. All curiosity to know-is strangely but gently stifled. "All is now and now is forever." Now is, and that now is beyond knowing now and forgetting later. "You do get but you [are given to] forget!" he pauses, "forget and forlorn you feel; you ache for the *amalaki,* right? I shall give you more than that! I shall throw them into your lap. Catch them, if you can!"

A flower
That falls
Seen and heard,
Tender to the touch,
Ravishing to the eye,
Falls into the
Light at the centre!
Can you get a flower
Without the plant?
Without the plant
Becoming a tree?
Without a tree
The fruit is not!
So see these
Leaves rustling
Delicately, kept for long,
Long time to prolong
The longing for the
Light at the middle
That the Sun and the Moon

Churn into being,
The leaves light up the pathless land.
The leaves that rustle when
The Buddha lands under their shade!
The leaves that leap with joy
When the Paramahamsa dances
In a daze under the tree in
Panchavati! The leaves that crazy
With love, lie in his hands now,
To land in my lap!
They glow gleefully,
Grinning at me:
"the fun this time
is for you!" they
rustle and reveal.

More fun-filled things fill the hours. Is he the Kalpataru? Is he
going to grant the spectrum of nature in miniature? It seems so.

For, from the sacred ash
And sanctified hands
A flower comes:
The fairest I see.
Then comes a jamoon;
Followed by a root
Named after Bengal itself:
Potato [Bangala dumpa]

I sit lost in the unrolling of the vastness of nature in her
concretions. When I least expect, he gives patram, pushpam,
phalam... leaf, flower and fruit. They look at me winking with
hardly concealed irony in their eyes! "You think you need to know
him in reality! Know him as the One behind the Many. So here he
is, see!"

The flower that
Blooms is his
Eye!
The fruit that
Flows from the

Flower is his flesh;
The root that comes
From the seed is
His *sukshma sharira*
Becoming the *sthula sharira.*

"Becoming?" the question hardly arises. Becoming is only for lila not for nitya. "I am the same Krishna, I am the same Radha, the same Siva, the same *salagrama.* Continuity is; break appears to be; and since break isn't, there can hardly be neat beginnings and conclusive endings.

The *salagrama*
Appears solid
So that you know
What is liquid;
Krishna appears,
So that you learn
Who Rama is;
And both come
Together in
"Sri Ramakrishna"
they lived apart
in time and decide
now to come together
as the Eternal One
the Great Swan!

And "I come since they are in a mood to witness the play from a distance. I body myself this time as re-membered Rama and Krishna but re-designed as One," so that, I add to myself, the Many remain many behind the curtain! They wink through him but remain wary. None should catch them in this body. As far as he can help. Obviously this time he doesn't.

The Siva-salagrama
Turns in his hand;
Perched on the thumb
It exultantly
Escapes from all support!
Incredible, hanging from

His thumb, hanging
In space! Turning
On his thumb. Supportless
On the thumb of the One
Who is the Succour and Support of the Many.

Turning inside! The something which turns inside transfixes me. Are they the sun and the moon? The stars twinkling with subdued smiles writ all over their faces? At this delightful confinement in the space of the *salagrama,* their space-transcending, time-free frames. Do I see the micro of the macro? The miniature of the *brahmanda* miraculously compressed? Marvellously modelled for the mind-construct to exult and escape the environs of its own alleged creation of reality? The *grama* and the *salagrama,* the city and the icon hanging in space, time collapse.

"Nothing to marvel at! Nothing to prize as a unique surprise. All that exists is a miracle. No more a miracle than this *amalaki!*"

Warmth floods the eyes that look at that fruit. See! Behind that tiny one is the earth that holds it in its bosom; the sun that dances in its veins with warmth. The moon that sheds its tender rays. The water that engulfs it in its coolness. The One who brings water to where the fruit lies in its seed form. The One who oversees all these as so many limbs of his/her own *virat rupa.*

Can anything be more miraculous than this most natural *amalaki.* My being is its becoming. It cannot cease its becoming; that would be, for me, to cease being. That is unnatural. The *Ida* and the *Pingala* have to go on.... Breathing with ceaseless breath. And

He throws the *amalaki*
By the sleight of the love-hands
Into my lap!
I lap it up with
Ravenous hunger
That, this time, is REAL.

"*Patram, pushpam, phalam...*" "I know," he says, "take this *toyam,* water, too!" he places a chalice of *charanamrita* in my hands.

I hear the intoning of a *sloka:* "Just as ether is all pervading and unaffected by contact, so also does the ever conscious self pervade everything, without being affected in any way. I am that self." Memory races across centuries. Sage Sankara's *Hastamalaka Stotra* flashes in the mind.

20

THE MUSIC OF THE LOCKED LIMBS

Words of the mute-articulate lover of the Mother breaks the muted barrier and speak in my being's ear:
I meditate on
The Red One,
Who lives on the
Land beside Kampa/Ganga river,
Wearing as her garment
The very worlds, which
Filling Siva with terror,
Shatter his courage!
Kampa is Ganga. The rivers are transposed. I wear the words-the *matrikas* as my garments and the world of the Mute Mother becomes mine.

My *sahasrara* is her [should I again say his] *lilakshetra*. The tree of my body holds her being; her *Kanchi* is the middle. And my puny body is no longer puny. The cosmos itself turns on the Meru in my *deha*. Where else shall I get a more pliable pilgrim centre than my own transfigured body? From top to toe, from *sahasrara* to *muladhara,* she presides. And all that I desire, decipher and do arise from the in-between *kshetras*. Like an expert lover who knows the knots of passion in the body, she plays on those knots-in my body and loosens them. They, strangely, languish in the midst of love!

Oh, my! How transporting is her/his touch. Is there ecstasy! Yes, there obviously is. But ecstasy that welcomes the body but makes no fetish of it. No thirst for the thrust that thrills but throttles the body by its own noose. Deflated, the body lies dead. That deflation is dispensed with. The urge for union is displaced by the surge for communion; deflation becomes deferral, endless deferral. The lotus in the *sahasrara* rises from *muladhara* but allows no descent, no penetration.

Is that a description, a map merely and no truth? The truth of poetry and no truth of the poetry of the body, or rather, the body of poetry? Endless play on words ends only on and in words. But if they end on and in the Word, then words have done their job. Their alotted job; as the alphabet of the Mother but with her as the alpha and the omega. That is the only thing that one has to bet on-to win her in the race.

"Words should be charged with the Mother, you know that ?" he asks. He asks but [I say] I do not jump in to answer. I learnt the hard way; angels of the earth rush where "fools" of heaven hesitate. Hesitation here is meditation. Meditation that is the only medication to mind's manifest misery of hurry. Even then I fall into the trap often. Ever since I see him I am wary; aware of the abyss. Questions put by him, I realise, have answers that only his words can formulate. "Words should be charged with the Mother," he says again and refrains from adding, "you know that?"

I relax with immense relief. Relief but not cessation of alertness. To relax in his presence is to be re-lax: recharge your laxity with life and energise into awareness. To allow the fish joyful movement. Released from the *mrinmaya patra,* the pot of clay, the *jalapushpa,* the fish, swims in the *chinmaya samudra:* the ocean, the sea of consciousness. That is how I relax-re-lax-in his Presence.

No further words follow. Since words stop flowing, the gates of *dhyana* fling themselves open. Gates? Yes, there are gates. Those are gates of the body. When they are taken off their hinges, the gates in the body swing open. They need no hinges, no *indhana,* fuel. Their fuel is not funnelled, not fanned properly by us. It spills over and burns, stings like a scorpion. Poison makes closes the gates. Stop the spill over, the gates rotate without even the fuel. No scaffolding is necessary for installing the beloved in the body.

"You have a tendency to be obscure, cruelly cryptic," I ask myself. Yes, I have to be. Even greater and wiser ones are like that. "*Sringaradvaita tantra siddhantam*," says one struck dumb by the mystery, dazed by the miracle. "The dialectic of erotic oneness that is the warp and the woof." For that to happen, nothing else should happen in and outside the mind. Absolute oneness. Oneness that devours everything that smacks of two.

A sudden tingling sensation in the spine. A movement of thought and a melody of form urge me: "Watch things. Words do not always watch. They often show wrong time. Either delayed or advanced. For, the time comes when your watch[ing] is least prepared."

How he changes moods like a chameleon changing colours! The dense dark forest denies entry to everything. "Let me insulate it," he seems to say. Bar it from everything that threatens... threatens? Yes, indeed. Good things are always at the mercy of the mean ones. Nature delights in providing this challenge. Everyone has to face it. (Don't I know?)

I already lose my eyes, a loss which makes him register in the sight. This loss is the Nandi, the preamble to the *nataka* the play. See how he sits on the ground. *Sthirasana,* firm posture, never seems to have a more glorious exemplar. For that to happen for you look at the supple, the delicate, the finely-honed body. The limbs bend without breaking. Not just firm; but firmness which goes with fluidity. Not like a rod of unbendable iron; but like a huge twig of the neem tree!

I didn't notice it until now. He is stark naked. Not a stitch on. "Ugh! What a nuisance!" I hear him uttering. But I do not connect it with this throwing away the only piece of *dhoti* he wears with difficulty. To save the prurient and the puritan from embarrassment. But when Mother possesses all prurience flies in fear. The child is always naked before the Mother. The lover disrobes delightedly the bride whom he himself decks earlier! (h himself tells me!)

Digambara is preliminary to the passport for entry into Chidambara. Nakedness that is not nudity; nudity that is not nakedness. That is the way one has to put it. What joy to be rid of all *kanchukas,* cloaks that clothe and conceal! Ecstasy in, exulting in one's primal body, the body that has no clothes made yet that can conceal it. The limbs glow but with no cupidity. The organs are flowering forth in splendour, lotuses that bloom into being, blasting themselves through the *malas,* the mud and mire, the taints that are on tenterhooks to catch the *Pasu.*

I can't hear it immediately. Some word is on the lips. Barely audible, scarcely pronounced even. Only the subtle *mudra* of the lips betray the word being formed. The letters are caught on the movement of the lips and not in the alphabet that is pronounced. *Matrikas,* the seed words, are not pronounced; they are announced; rather, they enunciate themselves and thus get announced. Words do by lips what the Mother's body, the Srichakra, does through visible lines! *Para vidya* can only permit *paravak.*

"Rang!" I hear it now. The alphabet becomes the diagram. The diagram is invisible just as the word is inaudible. Yet they are both visible and audible. Visible! I notice now. Slowly, as if from nowhere, but actually from all the directions, flames of a fire that is furious appear. They look like Bhairavas who keep sentry while the Lord of the Bhairavas meditates. I see the flame more than the forms. Blazing flame as if in a *yajna* someone is pouring clarified butter into it; crackling, the flame leaps up. Do I see it right? Yes, a *mandala,* a circle forms round him.

He sees nothing. Even when eyes are not closed. No smile appears on the lips. No word, either, as earlier. Stone-like he sits. The flames grow; they gather incredible strength. Seed words that sprout into leaves, branches that seem to be the flame. The flames allow entry to none. You can't leap across and fall into his lap. Even his children are kept out. Even when you don't mind getting singed, you can not enter in there. That is secret.

I can only look from near: only that concession is given. Can't we, children of the Mother, disregard the fire and rush in, into his arms? Do you want to really? Then you will know. The fire and

flame that sing for him, singe and scorch you. The sport is not for
all, though all are his children. The *lila* is for those who feel the
nitya in their guts. Those who are totally, unabashedly naked!

I refrain thus, poised on the fringe, near but not near to get
burnt. Near enough now to hear. I am frozen with fear and even
terror. Struck by the sounds that I hear. Sounds that are from his
body. Unmistakably audible, clearly identifiable. Sounds of locks
being locked—firmly, sternly—with keys that only the Mother
keeps. Keys that lock this way only to open that way. At the joints
of the body, they lock in. "Nothing doing; no movement, until the
kreeda, the sport is over!" He is under her lock and key. My ears
attuned to sounds, at first do not tune to the soundproof, silent
locking systems.

The body is now much more firm, infinitely more relaxed
with the locks on. Even the locks of his long hair (so long that they
are brooms that clean the *malas* of the "clean ones" that come to
the temple!) are locked in. They cease to rustle in the wind.
"Picture horse" they say. This is "portrait locks of hair." (Worthy
of a Picasso!) A radiant aura settles around; the flames withdraw
to the background but do not extinguish themselves. They enjoy
the heat that generates from him; he enjoys the warmth that comes
from them.

I watch and watch him: to come to me. To come with no locks
on, no keys needed. Just like that, and say, "Come let us lock
ourselves in! and lose the key; intentionally throw the key away.
Get locked up for ever and ever!" (Tinsel talk? Not if you know!)

"Should I say it again? How many more assurances will you
ask for? It is funny, isn't it?" he literally thunders.

I sit in a daze. Where are the flames, the locks, the keys, the
music of the locked limbs? "What have I not said, child?" says the
Thunder, again, this time with sorrow more than laughter!

21
TRICKSTERS

O Mother!
Thy desire, *kama*
Impels a throb, *spanda;*
That initiates
A vibration, *nada*
They crystallise into
A point, a dot, *bindu:*
The triangle of the *bindus*
Triggers all that exists
Into being;
Thou exist
As *jagrat, swapna, sushupti,*
As *iccha, jnana, kriya,*
As *mana, matri, meya,*
And as *turiya,* beyond
All the *Triputis;*
Thou art the Child,
Thou art the Comely One,
Thou art the Terrifying One;
In thy womb
I too am
A throb
A vibration
A point;
Thrown out

From the womb,
Where can I land
But at Thy
Lotus Feet!

"Oh! You are at your game again!" he laughs. "I must say I am impressed."

I want to tell him that this is one way I could impress him. Tell him that this way I relate to him. One among a long, long line of lovers of the Mother: some aware, some forgetful; some callous beyond apparent redemption. But it is her/his play. Nothing to regret, so nothing to rejoice. Regret for what? Rejoice at what?

"I wish I know your language! You know it so well. But, alas, words fall flat...," he says with what appears as conviction. He is back, behind the curtain, directing the play. "OK I shall also play along," I feel like telling him. "And I am not good even with words; even that has been doubted, My Lord!" I want to tell him, somewhat flippantly. I refrain. In the present mood, there is nothing to tell, nothing to hear.

"Are you depressed?" he asks. Why words, even from him? That is my response. Should he not be aware that tell your depression to others and you nurse it into a seed. Once a seed, you can hardly stop it from sprouting. Takes deep root and then where are you? In an abyss without exit. A corridor without a door. A labyrinth in which you turn and turn only to get more and more trapped. As if you don't have enough of your "own" trapping; besides the trapping (tracking?) from the "owner" who seems to "own" you.

Extraordinary unrest seizes me. Restive is a mild word. Racked, distraught, unhinged, broken beyond what seems to be irreparable. Has Chinnamasta cheerfully cast her shadow? Has she cut at the root of coherence, order, synchronicity, correspondence? Has she commanded that chaos should reign in all its glory? That every vestige of even faith should be cut to pieces with her scalpel?

I can no longer even sit-quietly, even for a minute. The Ganga too, seems belligerent: "Just touch me, and see what I will do: you shall get drowned, I assure you!" Panchavati is shrieking with voices that I never heard before. Strange shouts! Exultant, unnerving; thirsty for my blood? They grow in volume. Voices without forms; words without the tongue to utter them. They all seem celebrating. Celebrating my decomposition, my dismemberment? Excited at the prospect of my extinction? Gloating over gathering one more to their gang?

Quiet everywhere except for me. Have I created my own cosmos? Everywhere—wherever I see—there is silence. Exhausted after a day's toil, the toiling ones are sleeping. I envy them their slumber: how lucky they can sleep with all these voices shouting all around? Are they deaf? Or, is my hearing a hallucination?

I feel like taking him to task. (Even he!). Have it out with him once and for all. "No more playing with me. I am sick and tired. I have had enough of this. Tell me the truth." About myself, about himself. This time I won't leave him. Draw everything from him. Even if I cannot stand the truth; even if I break in the process. Enough of metaphors, of analogies, of cryptic puzzles. I have no intelligence left to decode those. Rather, not enough patience for that. (Whether I should claim intelligence or not is a different matter.)

Like a monkey bitten by a scorpion and possessed by a devil-that sums up the mood. ("You are using metaphors." "Yes, for myself, not for him.") I roam in the courtyard with people sleeping all around. Siva, too, is inert. Even Radhakrishna, the sleepless lovers, are (or seem) asleep. The lapping of the river, against the banks, seems accelerating. As if Ganga is bent on drowning me, and in the process, drown everything.

Lost, lost, lost! With nothing to reclaim, no one to redeem. I do not even feel like asking for any support, any succour. "One has to look after oneself," he says. "No promises are possible here," he adds. Isn't it frightening to be alone? To be absolutely alone, left to drift in an ocean with no direction? With nothing known to look back to? With none in the present? The anguish that results is real. Whether s/he is real or not—this is for real. You cannot get away from it. One's agony is real; the agony is agonisingly palpable.

"You are strangely rebellious these days," he whispers. Goose pimples spring all over my body. Where did he come from, again. Materialised himself? I thought he disappeared so that I have quiet for my quiet desperation. His coming is unnerving. His going equally so. He vanishes, just like that. "Strangely restless," he repeats. "There is something that seems to catch you by the neck!" Yes, I know what that something is. "Not something," he better know: "someone catches me by the neck!"

The Other and
The Mother
Play tricks
They are the
Timeless
TRICKSTERS.
Tricks that
Are timeless
Kept for use
When a victim
Comes along!

Even in unrest, rhyme comes through. Words do not seem to vanish. Knowing me thoroughly, can't he say "put out your tongue" and write some—what do they call?—*beejakshara* so that everything that is enervating evaporates? "Yes, I can!" he says promptly. "But you lost your tongue in words." And adds, "you think if you write "longing" longing for me comes, automatically."

There is no need to tell me what I think. No one better knows what I think than me. And not much longing, too, if I am honest with myself. I am fascinated more than committed. He fascinates me and, intriguingly, out of this fascination comes most of my (could I say) love for him. This fascination—turned love is a peculiar thing. One hardly knows its nature.

Since I know not its nature, depression sets in. Deep, deep depression. I roam everywhere. The Ganga Ghats do not give me respite. The *bhajans* in the temple bore me stiff. *Satsangs* I shun religiously. Only one thought plagues me: why am I so uneven in my awareness? Why is this awareness discontinuous? What prevents me from knowing and, more than knowing, experiencing the Reality that s/he so obviously is? "I hold the key and I know when to use it!" he reiterates. I leave it there. I do not have energy to extend the key business further. If he wants to keep it a secret, so be it. I have no quarrel. But I have an urge to know without my attempt to qualify for that knowledge, isn't this strange?

I am myself a strange creature. Experiencing the real, I expose myself to dreams. And dreams end up in fantasies. Fantasies fan visions. All seem mixed up to me. Is there no way to sift them? Or, is sifting impossible, since they are like *tantra,* a long, unending thread?

The depression, for instance. Why does it go on and on? Is there no terminus where it can get off my back? Is there some sanctity attached to it? The more I analyse it, the more it tightens its grip on me. Should I then stop all analysis? And admiration for all the brilliant analysts and analyses? I hardly know.... Let me simply submit to depression. Even despair is an ocean in itself. Part of the sea of consciousness. Perhaps the waves may throw me on the banks into the bosom of the Source. Let Thy will be done.

22

DROWN ME IN THE MAGIC OF THY MAYA!

The waves swallow me. I willingly submit myself to them. Better to be swallowed than saved. If you get submerged here you may emerge there: that is my fond hope. No fear of losing oneself. No loss in that sense is conceivable. For, when one gains nothing then where is the question of losing something? To gain nothing is the aim of everything that we do. Even depression has to exist. Manure for the flowering of a tree. The tree that has its autumn, and its spring, too.

Who can predict the entry of something that fills the nothing? The space in the jar is the place where something can enter. Not the walls, but the emptiness of the room is what is needed. You cannot sit on a wall. You can sit in a room on the ground. But without the walls, the space does not give the illusion of being enclosed. Without the emptiness of the womb, the child cannot enter the space of the Mother. The one is linked to the other.

Depression prefaces delight. Delight in the deep-seated duality that divides things for the drama of the Mother. Where is delight to be had except in drama? Play alone makes pleasure possible so that pleasure's copy can be compared to the original— the original that keeps itself hidden, so that the copy can pass off as the original.

The mild morning rays of the sun dispel the mist. The river flows exultantly. No longer threatening to devour, to swallow me. "You can't control the waves! But learn to surf!" she seems to say.

Surfing is all that one can do perhaps. But to do it even without
needing the water of the river! The mind races towards the reality
of all that is. The reality that is illusion; until illusion is invisible,
the reality is not perceptible. Welcome the illusion so that reality
comes dancing behind. Then embrace both. *Maya sakti* is *sakti*,
too.

Why should he come? To save us from the snares of *maya*?
Then glory be to *maya*! She makes his/her descent a reality:
Mother!
Thou art the
Great Void
Devoid of dullness.
I meditate upon
That stillness
Of your Void
And the Void
Reflects me
In all my splendour
In all my sorrow,
In all my being.
That which is still
Seems to move
With me, in me,
For me.

I am swallowed by the waves of her *karuna*. Her infinite
mercy. Mercy that is sometimes the face of cruelty, indifference
and detachment. "One has to go through all these," she seems to
say. "Can't you go through all these for my sake," she whispers.
"If I am sure, it is for your sake," I feel like saying. "I willingly
invite the illusion," she says with clinical honesty.

I remain, myself, incorrigibly insensitive. A stupor seems to
overtake me. Even his call I miss. Did he mean that I should miss
it? Is it his deliberate design? A kind of drastic operative design to
cut at the roots of all inertia, something that appears as inertia, but
can as well be illumination? A simple shuffling of the coins and
you know that this is also possible.

He comes out of the room. He appears uniquely cheerful. The sheer joy of being seems to possess him. Of course, we do not know what happens in samadhi. But if his behaviour *immediately after* is any clue, then there is something exceptionally, incredibly enjoyable inhering in the experience. One minute he seems lost; another he is back with a bounce, a zest for living itself, rather than for *samadhi*.

That is how he is now, as he emerges from the room. I see him from a distance. Not very far but not close enough for him to see me. This vantage point suits me. To remain in the background, unnoticed, anonymous. This is not humility; I do not have much of it. It is self-consciousness. The awareness that anonymity is a quality that has to be deliberately cultivated. Otherwise, the play cannot be enjoyed. If my real identity is not known, to that extent and until then, even if a name and form are there, I will never know myself. Identity breaks name and form, dissolves them; and until that is achieved, no real seeing is possible. The *drig-drishya-viveka* comes to my rescue.

Facing his
Beloved river
He is flushed
With exuberant
Joy!
The river's
Radiant reality
Roots his roving eye
The urge for
Flight, the
Natural soaring
Of the Swan,
Is neutralised.
Strangely
The voice reaches
My ears:
Ma, ma, ma
O Mahamaya!

Be gracious
And overwhelm me!
Drown me in
Thy magic!
I need desperately
Thy soul-bewitching
Maya!
Come Delusion!
Come Infatuation!
Devour me
And dance
With ecstasy
Thy deluding power
Is what I need
Most!
Drown me in that
Deluge.

Evoking *maya* to annul his being? Inviting the Enchantress to hypnotise him by her splendour? Inconceivable. I cannot believe that he is doing this: not asking for *viveka* and *vairagya*, not seeking *tyaga* and *tapas;* not even *bhakti* and *bhajan.* Is he again gone off the rocker? Why does he expose me to such contraries? Why pick on me and spare the other children? Isn't this enough to unhinge one? One tries to free oneself from the clutches of the Great Enchantress. And here he is, asking *Mahamaya* to overwhelm him. As if the very image of her being doesn't create enough terror. He himself makes me, quite often, frozen with fear, when he sings in that voice of his which carries in itself all the terror, when he wants it. "Can I not simply roll up all the worlds like a mat!" he says. Not with a twinkle in the eye but with hardly concealed terror. I wish to run away from such moments. I am used to *soumya* not *roudra.* I relish *roudra* in abstraction but when it strikes me in the face, I am transfixed. The spine requires extra access of energy to face it. Once the transfusion with terror begins to possess the body, terror begets surpassing tranquillity. Cutting through my reverie, he shouts again:

Come Mother!
Show me Thy
Deluding Form.

As if this is too mild an invitation and, therefore, may not evoke any response he plunges into singing. Have you heard him sing? Have you at any time listened to the breeze that caresses your feverish body, the *malaya* wind that cajoles you into her lap? Listen to the breeze, I say. Not feel it on the skin! That is how, quite often his singing is. Your breath regulates itself and flows along the song and, slowly, imperceptibly, the breath itself becomes the song. The melody moulds the breath and tunes the heart-strings gently, not taut or tense.

But don't run away with the idea that this is the only way he sings. When he chooses, he drives away the demon of sanity. He is then drugged, totally de-ranged. De-ranged! All ranges of classification, categorisation, calculation collapse. Then the singing merges into dancing. The dancing dervish! What strides he dances with! With what vigour the feet fight for freedom from the pull of the earth. Or else, the earth will shake at his *nritya*! *Pranaya* dissolves into *pralaya*. Adoration slides into apocalypse. You shiver, your bones rattle, your body is freed from fear and you rise in the air and dance with him. Levitation? Yes, achieved through the Mother's Pretext Pill that is irresistible: Love and love evoked through terror is the Pill that pierces, percolates and pulls the Presence before your eyes:

Mad is my father,
Mad is my mother.
Can the son be sane?
I am mad, too.
The Dark One is
My mother's name.
And my father?
What can he do
Except strike his cheeks
And make a hollow sound
Ba-ba-boom, Ba-ba-boom!

See my mother
There all action is.
Drunk to the dregs,
Reeling in intoxication
She falls—
Across my poor
father's bare body.
He sings, now naked himself:
My mother roams
About nude!
Who is the one
Who calls her shameless?
Let that one come
Before me: I shall
Pluck his eyes out
And give new ones.
Then he will see
My father and my mother
Are both nude:
But they wear a
Garland of skulls.
Even then I
Roar with laughter
When my mother's
Shrieking voice
Fills my nude father
With terror!
Come mother
Delude me
Like my father!

The dance becomes a frenzy now. They form a circle round him lest he escape from their midst. Do his rope trick again. I am outside the circle. I am afraid to join. I thought I am dancing too. "That is the delusion I create to freeze your methods of detection," he shouts from the centre of the circle. I hear, since it is meant for me....

The inebriation is nearly over. Some order is restored. He is
still reeling and, I think, will fall if someone does not catch him. I
venture to go near. He winks and whispers: "Shall we eat
something?" Eat? Of all things, after this. "Specially after such a
thing," he nearly shouts. I am cowed down. A plate of sweets
materialises itself from somewhere.

How ravenously he eats! As if there is a cauldron inside, a
raging furnace that has to be constantly fed his delicate, tender
frame hardly goes with that hunger, I always feel. "You are so
thin! Why don't you eat some of this?" he asks. As in everything
else, I am shy about eating, too. Somehow I manage to swallow a
piece. "I cannot imagine...."

"I know; you can't imagine my invoking *Mahamaya*. You
cannot make head or tail of what I sing about my nude father and
my nuder mother. And, of course, you think that my hunger is
obscene!" I am cut to the quick. "No, not obscene! I didn't say it.
It certainly appears unusual to me." Can I not express what I feel!

He belches with satisfaction, almost smacking his lips. I
almost look away! He is amused: I must say intolerably amused.
As if one can get only amused with a child who thinks s/he is
precocious while, in fact, s/he is retarded! Or, rather he wonders
whether he should tell me or not what he wants to do. Is there a
great secret hidden? A mystery that is profound? Suddenly I recall
his telling me:

What is normal
For you
Is abnormal
For me;
What is moral
For you
Is immoral
For me;
What is open
For you
Is a secret
For me!

I put it down as fondness for the word, play—he certainly is
fond of it.

Behind my
Nudity is
A cloak;
I am not
Nude at all!
But then you
Have to see
It yourself.

He says. I keep quiet. Let the answer come in its own time, in
its own way. I shall certainly wait, waiting at least I think I am
good at. "You know what happens when I lose my consciousness?
I can't even say what I lose! When that happens, I am lost, totally
gone. Bathing in bliss, soaring in the sky; rolling in the waves that
engulf me. Earth and heaven, the body and the mind are in a state
of *laya*." He gropes for words: "Like a salt doll merging into the
ocean."

When on my own—that is,
At Mother's signal—or by
Your attempts, I descend,
It is difficult for me to
Re-cognise things. Things
Have to sort themselves out.
The magic of *Mahamaya*
Does not work, yet. Then I
Have a strong urge to plunge
Again, ascend again
Then, for your sake, for the
Fun of lila, I have to invoke
My Mother, the Great Enchantress
To keep me conscious; keep
Me at the threshold. Then
Praying to the Great Enchantress
Is the only way. Of course,
It is you who always pull
Me back!

I sit stunned at this reversal. We have to make all attempts to ascend; he tries desperately to descend! And for me, for you, for everyone who allows him to descend into his/her heart. But I take peculiar (even perverse) pleasure: "I am! My being has a logic! It is that that pulls him back! He just looks at the fun on the other side of the wall and with ecstasy dancing on his face, comes down to take us up the ladder, rung by rung!"

"As for my eating..." he hardly begins, when we see a boat anchoring before us at the ghat. People jump on to the banks. Two or three look straight: their faces are lighted up when they see him. He, of course, is radiant, rearing to jump into their arms, as it were. I am constantly intrigued by these reunions. As if they are together after *yugas*.

The first thing he asks, again, puzzles me: "Have you eaten anything? It is late in the night. Nothing will be available now. What shall I do?" he says helplessly. Genuine, touching helplessness, I thought. But they seem unconcerned: they don't look famished, at all. On the contrary, they look sumptuously fed.

"*Baba,* with you around, will any child go feeling hungry?" He keeps quiet. The devotee continues, "A marvellous thing. We don't know how such a thing can happen...." he is obviously trying to put in words something that words resist: an experience not of the ordinary. "We felt hungry, ravenously hungry. Coming on the boat we have, as you know, *baba,* hunger which can devour and digest anything. But nothing is available. Not even a roti; not even a piece of *jilepi.* And hunger so unbearable. As if someone entered inside and created that hunger! For fun to see how we suffer, how much we can bear." The devotee pauses, looks into his eyes strangely, as if trying to go beyond what they show, to what they do not.

"When we thought, we would faint, this thing happened. When and how, we hardly know. Sound of the belly being filled with food... two or three minutes. As if someone is eating for and in us. Then all hunger vanished. Vanished not like a magician removing it with a magic wand. But like someone who actually transferred his/her eating to us.... We don't need anything now...."

Baba looks at the river and then looks at me: "As for my eating...." No need for him to complete the words. The *chelas,* his children, did it.

I eat, myself, all this with ravenous hunger....

23

THE KHADGAMALA

"Do you think it is a joke to love me," he asks me point-blank. No
mincing the words. No politeness in the tone. No compromise is
allowed for comprehension. He means exactly what he says.

"Do you love that dead body?" he asks me abruptly. A corpse
is floating down the river. Lapped up by the waves. They are
licking the body with love. "Do you love that? He repeats. "Can
you float down the river like that body, dead to what the waves do?
But alive to me?"

He seems in a mood for a series of questions. I can't say that
the questions register. As so often it happens, I am floating on
waves of my own: *tarangas* that rise and fall like the ebb and tide
at the sight of the moon/the man. Sighting him is enough. You are
excited. All that is cited in the lover's texts is true, I know now.

I am enslaved
By her enchanting
Form, dwelling
In Dakshineswara:
The contours of
Her body conceal
Secrets that only
Those who have
No carnal eyes
See!
They are windows
To the wonders

That the world
Does not need to be
Discarded, to be
Discovered!
The reverie, this time, does not seem to affect him. All
reveries are waves of the same river. Did I feel enchantment or
love? Is there any variation between the two? Isn't love itself an
enchantment, beyond compare? Are not both the two faces of one
frame? I am sure they are. "Don't be too sure about these things,"
he is now gentle. The admonition is mild; more a caution than a
warning. "You must check before you choose," he adds and looks
through his usual lens: si-lense.
   Check? Where else? Isn't s/he an encyclopaedia of the secrets
of love that lasts and lasts. ("Shades of ad. Slogans in your words,"
he whispers. Be careful!) That teases me. (All that teases-coming
from him-always teaches.) I do wish to check. But how and when
and where? "Have you fallen in love?" he teases again. I nod my
head; hesitant, reluctant to admit in words. "There is, of course,
hope if you fall in love!" Hope?
   "Yes, hope. And remember this: fall in love with your
beloved; but rise in it to reach me!" He is plain; straight forward.
"Me," he rarely uses it:
   fall in love
   with your beloved,
   rise in it
   to reach
   ME.
   I am slightly rattled. I thought that falling in love is the
greatest. Nothing else matters. That is itself falling in love with
him, I thought, I think. "Almost all fall in love, but few, only the
blessed few, love," he varies the teasing.
   "Mother once showed me the difference," he says, after a
pause. "So what? I haven't seen it? What I myself see matters to
me. Not what you saw but what I see.... Not what your mother
showed you but...."

"What I show you... right?" he completes the words. "Yes. That is what I mean." "That is fair enough," he admits. "But I still leave it to the Mother.... Perhaps, she may help us out."

There love rests. I too leave it there. We sit close. The stars glint in the distance. Strange! they seem so many eyes eager, themselves, to see what he shows. Lidless, patient for the Paramahamsa's *prema tantra.* "If the sun comes, he will pluck our eyes. Let all that has to happen, happen soon!" they pray. This is my plea, too.

Sitting close has impact (if, at all, he enters into a pact to sit close to you). The first thing I notice is the rush of energy into the body. An aura of light enters you, encircles you. Even insulates you from everything. Freezing of the frontiers, *dik bandhana.* That is what it is. I say, the body. Yes, the body feels the rush. Drooping, drowsy one minute: in a split second it is like a horse rearing to go. Like words that rush through, racing to the hand that reaches them to paper and ink.

The bird watcher waits. Always alert; but since he does not want to catch the bird he is relaxed. Absence of aim makes for and accelerates alertness without anxiety. Anxiety to focus on one thing and exclude others thereby. Anxiety to concentrate and thus miss the centre beyond the concentrated one. I instinctively know the thing. Analogies fail me. I find no example to exemplify.

Like my situation now. I am told that loving is different from falling in love. That one experiences the love that is no falling as distinct from the love that is falling (and rising?) Fall? Fall of man in the garden? The garden itself unable to guard the innocent. And what is this fall? Is it the fall of whatever it is that is related to love? Is it some secret exercise that makes you stop at the moment when fall is instinctive?

"Relax. And do not waste your energy on this kind of speculation. You seem addicted to the body as *tantra* and not *tantra* as the body...," he says. He always has this tendency of cutting into the sheaves of your thoughts. Quite disconcerting. I do not, of course, find it necessary to talk. And I cannot consider his words as "talk". They are directions, rather directives.

A deep sense of peace and well-being seems to enter me. Unique clarity, equally singular sanity, invigorates my being. Like waves that float you gently. Ebb and tide seem to vanish. The river flows evenly. It seems delighted in the sheer diversity that floats on her bosom. One of those moments that burn into your memory. Moments that are seeds seeping into your consciousness. Seeds that are not *dagdha beeja,* burnt seeds. I do not even know how to put it to you. As, you must have noticed, so rarely happens. Or, rather, the rarity is in our perception and reception. The well-being always is. You cannot take away or add one drop to it. Full it always is; the comparative and the superlative are banished into the vaults of *vyakarana.* Continous present tense—without being tense about the past or the future.

How I enjoy those quiet moments! Insurance against the fatality of depression. But the premium is quite heavy. Surrender to all that is, all that he is, all that she is. After depression comes the deluge of redemption. A depression in the bay of your body and mind is necessary for rain to inundate you, to pull you by your roots. The tempestuous wind wipes out everything that interfered with a rich harvesting. I feel like getting into the river and, in fact, plunge to its depths. The shadow of fear of drowning in the depths flees.

I go down the ghat, slowly. I descend to the river. What a descent! I don't see even the steps! I think there are none. You glide into the river waiting for ages to gather you into her arms. How invigoratingly cool the water is! The spine feels the first shock. Like fire that does not burn but warms, wind that gently fans and does not sweep you off your feet, like touch that triggers but does not explode; like smell that intoxicates but does not inebriate. And, wonder of wonders, eyes are not—any longer—on fire. They see but do not "sense" what they see. The eyes of a camera that registers everything with no preferences of her own. With no special pattern bestowed on anything. They are vibrant but neutral, not voyeuristic, vibrant! That is the word that sums it up.

Vibrant without volition; vital without the body rushing to arrest that vitality. And claim it for itself, and freeze it. The vitality

flows and strangely I notice that that flowing is no flow at all.
Neither upwards nor downwards. Neither reaching out to the
explosion, in the *sahasrara* nor reaching down, exhausted to the
muladhara.

"That is where the dance is!" he whispers without words. He
is already transfigured. Oh, my! I look at him again. rub my eyes
and see. Not with wonder as earlier but with wide, unperceiving
eyes. Where is he? I see a huge shutter open itself. See through the
lense. You have to see only like that. Only that way of seeing is
seeing. All else is eyeing, goggling, peering through. Such eyes
need surgery. Then only they see without eyes. Like seeing in
dreams with eyes closed. Then is it a dream? Yes and no! Vision?
Yes and no. Fact? Yes and no. Fiction? Yes and no. How can you
predicate contraries of an experience that lasts and thus lets itself
out of all your attributions and predications? That is why yes and
no. *Satya* is always *viruddha* when you categorise. Experience it,
all contraries fly! Take to wings and fly, far, far away.

The Mother beckons to him. Imperceptibly she comes: like
youth to an adolescent. No date is fixed, no time is earmarked.
From the bowels of the being's earth she blooms. She comes like
that. That is why such a coming does not startle you. Expected yet
a surprise that soothes and smoothens your taut nerves—if they
are still tense. Which is doubtful.

"If you have the kind of eyes I gave you, then see!" "If?" Is
there still doubt? "From my side, no," s/he says. From your side,
check. That is what it means, check. So much caution? Is there
something terrible? Some secret, sordid rites of tantra? For a
minute I feel lost. A subdued laugh. This is Paramahamsa *prema
tantra,* she says.

I still am in the river. In the depths. How joyfully the fish
sport! How ecstatically they caress each other! With no one to
watch them, with no one telling them, "Do this and don't do that!"
Ecstatically they roam around in the ocean. Are there other sea
creatures to devour them? They hardly bother. They are willing to
risk death. For, they know that they land thereby only in the
Mother's lap. Then why spoil the swimming thinking of the

inevitability of sinking? I envy their nonchalance. I am jealous of their disregard of danger. *Matsya,* he tells me, is one of the five Ms. Whatever they are. I least bother. If fish are like this, then let me be one.

The scene unrolling before me, however, unnerves me. Oh, Mother! Where are you? What are you doing to me? Don't you want that I should be sane? What is this madness that overtakes the one whom I love most? Should I be subjected to this agony? To this incredible enactment?

Even in the icy waters of the Ganga, the heat from the flames that emanate from his body scorches me. I see his body burning, burning without let and go. The leaves on which he walks dazed, are scorched! They become ash! Even twigs are tinder! The heat is unbearable. He seems wracked with intolerable agony of a sheer physical kind. Have you heard of anyone whose body ignites, particles of dust as if they are inflammable, highly explosive! When they get in contact with that frame they are inflammed!

Desperate with this heat that burns his body he plunges into the river. "Ma Ganga!" he shouts in agony and jumps. Strange! Gangamayi withdraws in haste; afraid that she will herself be scorched. "I can't bear it, child! I can't! try as I might, I just can't" I can vouch for Ganga's haste in retreating. Can she go against the wishes of the Mother of all? She wants him to be like that! Burn himself out like a candle for her. Annihilate himself if he wants to advance in her direction. Only the burnt body achieves the alchemy. There is no other way, no other way.

I am amazed; but I quickly consent: Yes I know that is the way. The body burns and burns before the miracle happens. And the miracle is that the body disappears. The registering of this heat is the real death that is prelude to birth in the Mother's womb.

He rolls on the ground. Someone has rubbed his body with sandalwood paste. The paste cracks like an enamel plate. The moment it touches the body it cracks; it loses its cool. It is, in turn, itself burning, adding to the burning in his body. "*Ma! Ma!*" is the only word that still manages to escape his cracked lips. One is frightened, really frightened that he could be so sure that Mother is around the corner—of his burning, of his suffering.

I stand and stare—from a distance. My body registers his burning! Am I also going to burn like that for him? Oh, *Ma*! Is it going to be the same? Have I to roll on the ground, too? Have I, also, to get my lips cracked? My hair singed? Even my heart croaks in its shell? Is there no other way?

Don't you hear Ramprasad telling you it is so? There is no other way. But I thought, I tell her, that is the way of the body that burns, that burns for the Beloved? The burning of the body that burnishes the lamp of love. "That is it; what else do you think it is? What you can't experience you can't imagine. And what you imagine is what the visionary body's wisdom is."

I know the Master is cryptic; the Mother is totally confusing. Between them they make me a zombie [as if you are not a congenital one]. I really do not seem to know what they together are saying. Yet I watch horror growing in me. For, to his body's burning, eyes' tears are added. Unending stream of tears that seem breaking themselves into sparks of burning fire! The eyes are closed, yet they flow through without let and hindrance. Can there be so many tears in the eyes? Can there be so much *sakti* in them that they roll on the ground only to rise in adoration and fall at the Mother's feet?

For, he is in the temple now. How did he escape my eye and rush into the temple? When? How? Does he know his way in the darkness? I laugh instantly at my question. The Dark One is his Darling Ma! How dare any other darkness come near? He is reeling, obviously drunk; the madya of the Mother must have gone to his head. He sways this way and that. I see no glass in his hands but a pitcher of specially brewed wine in his heart. Fermented for long and so intoxicating that a drop, let alone a sip, is enough to drown you. In that sense-less insentience he intones a melody to the Mother:

Ma!
Pierce through
The Prithvi in the *Muladhara,*
The *Jala* in the Manipura,
The *Agni* in the *Swadhishtana,*

The *Vayu* in the *Anahata,*
The Akasha in the *Vishuddha,*
And *Manas* in the *Ajna;*
Ascend through my
Sushumna and sport
With this thy child:
In the solitude
Of the *Sahasrara*
Let us sport in
Ecstasy!

The song enthrals the *garbhagriha*. They are no words; they are flaming tongues that lick the body within the body into shape. They pierce through, penetrate through the luminous being's lovely body. But will the Mother yield so easily? Will she run, amidst her play, to this child, so effortlessly? She is stern but playful. Playfully stern, one can say. Let the child weep: that will do him good: *sadhaka balanam rodanam balam!* Weeping is strength for the child-*sadhaka!*

The song ceases. He stares intently. A streak of madness enters the eyes. Their colour changes. Blood-shot, furious with anger that makes me shake, cringe, to see those knotted brows frowning in inexpressible fury, irrepressible rage? That lovely face is now flushed with anger. Where did those tender tendrils of the eyes disappear? I see instead two burning coals blazing in fury; usually serene (though often mischievous) they are now shot with impatience at something that is near his grasp, yet eluding. Something well within view but seems out of reach. Or, rather within an arm's length but the arm needs a little bit of stretching. Stretching more than usual. And it is possible. Possibility is what makes it tantalising. Tantalising beyond point turns on its own and becomes in desperation, terrorising.

Does he want to terrorise the Mother into visible evidence of her presence? Presence in the depths of his being, held there everlastingly? Arrested and frozen forever in his sight, within the range of his vision?

My attention must have wandered for a split second. Otherwise I would have seen him wrenching the sword from the Mother. Imagine! From the Mother! Who wields it as her fancy roams cutting away at creation numberless times. Wielding it to slaughter the animals in humans, to shear the roots of ignorance. Not only to kill those who kill others but to protect the killer too! And he wrenches it in a minute and it is there that he disallows sight!

That wielding of the sword on his body in utter abandon to the Mother is something that one does not see. One just does it oneself. One wrenches it from him in desperate frenzy, in passion that reaches its peak, in zeal and jealousy that reach their zenith! Only then the Mother and the Master embrace each other and fold you up in their embrace! You sport with them! You play with them—a play that extends to eternity.

What are eyes for?
Only to see him
Swimming in the
Ocean that breaks
its bounds and
threatens to drown
him in herself!
He, the Siva,
Holds the sword
Firmly and cuts
The threatening
Waves of the deep darkness
Into two;
He cleaves at the
Closing—in waves of
Dhumavati, the
Dark One who advances
To overwhelm him.
He sharpens the
Sword with his *vibhuti*.
See how it shines
In splendour!

Splendour that
Transfigures my eyes.
Is it a sword
Or a garland
That he is placing
Round his own neck
While She sees it
All playfully?
Happy that the child
Is precociously innocent,
Knowingly ignorant,
Manfully child-like!

The radiance is riveting. And he re-covers [it]. I wait patiently. He merges yet emerges if only you wait! I wait. Neither patience nor impatience. Wait for nothing to happen. Everything happens now, always every moment.

"Yes! If you have the *khadgamala* it certainly is fun to love him."

24
THE MIRACLE THIRST

"I gather you perform miracles. Is it true?" I ask. "I want to see one." I add. He continues to play with the kites. Does he at all hear what I say? Does he imagine that anything that I say is so much... dirt? (He once told me that out of the Mother's divine dirt and dust only, her Elephant-faced son comes). Not worth bothering about. He is a kid, one has to wait for him to grow—is that what he thinks about me? Then he thinks right. I am desperate. I do wish to become his kid. I am in search of Mother.

No words from him. He lowers his eyes; they are not just playful this time. They are sly. Incredible: the way he changes his glances. Incorrigibly innocent, they become in a split second, incredibly mischievous, teasing, teasing beyond one's tolerance levels. He exasperates you by silence, annoys you with total absence of gestures. Next minute he makes you explode into laughter. Anger and annoyance: so much mist that moves away as the sun comes. You look at each other and you are lost! Lost in each other.

"I am fond of kites. You know that?" he asks. Ignoring what I say. "From my childhood I had a great liking for kites. My mother taught me. How to make kites." I am impatient. Even to the point of being rude—asking him "it is time you quit this, fooling us around like this...."But my word-kites always get grounded even before I start flying them. I love his fooling me. It's that simple. That's why I wait. (for more fooling? I don't just know. For his fooling me makes me feel less foolish than I think I am!)

"Mother and I make kites even now. Colourful ones. Small ones, big ones, square ones, round ones. I myself can not keep count of the shapes and sizes, of the colours and shades. Oh, I feel staggered when I see the variety." When he launches into this poetry thing, no one can stop him. A dreamy look, as if a hen is hatching eggs, comes into his eyes. Hatching, hatching and nothing but that. As if s/he wants to fill the *brahmanda* with her *anda* and *pinda*.

"Is it not time that you stop kite-making and tell me about your miracles?" The May-heat of Kamarpukur starts telling on my nerves. The pleasant morning breeze is now showing its other face: heat that makes the cool shade of the trees—on the bank of the lake before the house—not cool enough now. Lolling on the sand, pleasant then, is now losing that edge. I feel uncomfortable. Near breaking point.

"You require lot of knack to make the strings," he continues. He starts these monologues and you don't know where you are. He drives you to a corner where you have to listen, whether you like it or lump it. "I am for making the strings somewhat thin. Let the kites fly on their own in the sky without any strength in the strings," he says.

"But you know mother is stern. A steely look comes into her eyes. 'Nothing doing,' she shouts, 'they have to have strong strings. That's my order! You follow?'"

"I follow," he murmurs. "But me...," "I want to plead. Make them lighter, the strings. I say no and no it shall be. If every fellow wants to get away from my hand and fly on his/her own, then where is the play, where is the fun? I want my pound of flesh.' She says glaring at me." He subsides into silence.

Perhaps, he is not alert. A few kites snap the strings. See how majestically they glide away! She is overjoyed and claps her hands. He comes awake. "See *Ma*! They are getting away; the strings have come apart!" he cries. Irrepressible joy crosses the mother's face. Strange! I can't make head or tail of it. (Of course, I do not have a head, that I know; about tail, I wish I grew one!) She says she wants her pound of flesh and here she is clapping her hands when the kites get away. "Where can they go? They can only come to me. Wherever they think they go."

A sly look passes between the mother and the son. They burst out laughing, this time together. Uproariously, crazily, almost demented. They look at me and control themselves. I, of course, look away. Heat bothers me. With no miracle in sight the heat is hotter. The sands are burning.

I am thirsty. Unbearably thirsty. Thirst that can slay a camel. (You can slay a camel, not a cow, you know!) I get up to go to the pond and take some water into my hands and drink. Otherwise, I know I may even die from sheer thirst. "You can not take that water. It's not drinking water. Don't you know that?" he asks. I feel petrified. As it is the sun makes me feel stupid. And the thirst. Water everywhere and not a drop to drink! Is he again up to his pranks? The kites, the eggs, the string and now this.

"Shall I perform a miracle for you?" he asks. What a time to perform a miracle! Is he all right? Can slyness go further. I am dying for a drop of water, any water, and he asks, "Shall I perform a miracle?" "Shall I?" he repeats. "This is just the time; the ripe time; ripeness is all!" he winks at me and gives me back words that I gave him.

It is beyond me—to control. Even with him around I am about to explode. And at this moment he shouts to somebody in the house across the road: "Bring a glass of water, will you?" Perhaps no one is inside. Or, they are taking their own time. No water appears for quite some time. Of course, he is above all thirst and hunger. That glass must be for me. It must be for me. He is a man of miracles. He doesn't need these. He has built-in....

After what I think is a century but is just less than a minute, a small girl limping along with a glass of water appears. Why is she walking so slow? Most indisciplined these brats are, I explode inside. But the glass reaches him. And promptly he puts it to his lips and starts drinking! "Oh how thirsty I feel!"

And then he thrusts the glass at me: "Now drink, you too!" The gurgling sound of the cool water in my throat is music no miracle can create.

"I did perform the miracle, didn't I?"

Yes, the most miraculous water I have seen and drunk.

25

THE FISH IN THE WATER IS NO FISH!

"The fish in the water is thirsty!" he starts singing and chuckling. Feeling foolish, I refrain from joining him. Feeling foolish with real joy. Or, joyfully foolish. I seem to float on waves of continuing awareness. Nothing seems to come in the way. No cloud on the horizon to threaten. No ominous signals that shadows are near at hand. I bask in the glory.

How puerile words are: like animals they carry loads of fragrance but do not have the nostrils to inhale it. Can the word 'glory' convey to you the feeling I experience? Unless the word sheds its load and the fragrance slides into you, how do you know?

I see him everywhere, in everything. Not a metaphor. The reality. Everywhere he is showing himself. He is keen on showing himself everywhere. Is this true? I ask myself. I still cannot recover from the radiance of this reality. The miracle of this most marvelously natural reality. A body lying dead in the street seems overjoyed! "I can dance now! I shed all that holds me! I relinquish all that confines me!" it seems to whisper.

Every face I see, I see as a face flushed with the exuberance that the face itself hardly seems aware of. That is a wonder to me. Such a mart of joy you are and yet you cry and cringe, grovel and groan. As if you are nothing except that bag of flesh and bones. The pillow-case and the cotton: how we mistake one for the other and miss both.

Obsessed with the flesh
We miss the body;

Addicted to pleasure
We abandon the joy:
The flesh is the body
And pleasure is joy
Once you step in
And step out
Simultaneously,
In and out of the
Mother's maze.

I delight in the paradoxes. I literally live for them. The most carnal is the most contemplative; the most erotic is the eminently, the miraculously ecstatic. Do you need to possess a toy to play with it? Do you need the toy at all? The Mother makes toys of infinite variety. Some just inhale; some simply see; others delight in diverse ways of *sparsha*, the touch that transfigures and through transfiguration ceases to be merely herself: the touch. Seeing ceases to be seeing; touching ceases to be just that. Cease and seize: that is the secret.

The play on words is itself part of the vast play. Words have loads, yes. But something must be there, assigned to carry things. To bear the brunt. To even bear the womb itself. Womb has to be for words and forms to form themselves. The womb throws out in a dazzling display shape after shape. They cry and come out; smile and cry, cry and smile-to enter the womb again. The womb is the paradise: neither lost nor regained. It just is.

The infinite splendour of creation unnerves me. Its beauty arrests me. Saints come, scoundrels are ejected! Both with nonchalance by the mother. Her womb nurses no difference. If saints are born, so be it; if villains pulverise her womb and tug at it, let it be so. "Both are my *bindus*, the two points of my compass," she exultantly exclaims. If they bruise my breasts even when they suck them—so be it. "It is tender to love the babe that milks me. It is equally tender to dash its brains out—if I feel like it," she says.

I lie inert,
Inhaling the seed.
I suck the seed

So that the
Seed shall sprout.

But the seed is burnt, too, in some cases, rare cases. They nurse the Seed of all seeds and do not need any other. That is intriguing for everyone. It is a secret that few can bear and hold it to themselves. Not every seed need be nourished in the dark of the earth: it can be borne up and nursed in the light of the sky. The pull of the earth proves pointless, then. The sky beckons: "I shall hold it without spilling it into roots and flowers."

The body is. It houses everything. But ensures that it doesn't hold junk. Or, if junk is to be housed, you change its shape and size and place it inside. It can explode but take away the fuel.

Oh, my: how obsessive I am with the mother's being, her body, the *virat swarupa*, the *vishwa*, the cosmos. So harmonious and we, yet, try to better it. So beautiful, yet we pathetically try to beautify it. That is the pathos. Our attempt to better everything that is already good. Since they are replicas of her own rage for order, they-hardly-need something more.

Does he need anything more than what mother gives him? *Do roti, ek langoti, bas* enough. Nothing else to enjoy this vast, astounding adventure of life that she unrolls. "I am everywhere, I am everything." (Even *langoti* he sheds; strictly unnecessary, he says.)

"They say they saw you in Dakshineswar when I know that you were with me in Kamarpukur." I tell him, breaking the silence. "That's my pleasure. I have work everywhere. I have friends who want to see me wherever they are. And don't you think I should be wherever they want me?" I gape like a monkey. "Wherever they want me?" So I do not have any proprietary rights over him? "You have rights but like all rights...." he leaves it open. I desist from persisting for completion. Isn't he making me a victim of jealousy when he appears elsewhere even when he says- and I know—he is always with me? I would like to see him wherever he is. Not just with me alone. "If you move to the next lane, I must be with you. See anything but show to me what you see!" He is used to my peevish demand. "Spiritual greed is OK," he says.

How can he be at two places? Isn't it a miracle, a rare.... I hardly complete when he himself declares "a rare psychic phenomenon? You want to say. Do you?" Yes, that is it. That's what I think it is. "Everything is natural for one who has no other nature than the nature of nature, of mother's nature," he speaks firmly; not with his usual apparent frivolity.

> The fish floats
> In you,
> I float in the fish;
> The body enjoys you,
> I enjoy the body;
> The mind holds you
> I hold the mind;
> You hold the mother,
> The mother holds me.
> It's all *ulta pulta!*

I am used to his cryptic declarations. To his gaps, silences, fissures. One has to ferret them out. And one has to wait for that. It takes its own time. "Begin from where you are," he often tells me. And you must get used to his ways of seeing. See through, see with his eyes. Then only you can make sense.

I settle in the silence that always pervades that part of the land. Noises are there. They dare not enter that space. He insulates it— when he thinks noises are too noisy. "You know what Mother says?" he knows I know that I do not know. That I know how to stretch the thread without knowing the beginning and the end of the thread (does it have endings and beginnings?)

"Mother says so many things, shows so many things.... I do not always find the need to remember," he continues.

I like the quiet and the dark. It is quite dark. Birds settle in their nests. The leaves of the trees hug them close; "With us around, you shouldn't shiver!" the leaves say to the birds. The hollows of the trees are mansions for them. Cozy, warm, soft: what else does one require? The siren of the factory is silenced. Humans, too, hurry to settle in their dens. (Den? Are you sure the word is right?) Is it twilight or midnight? It hardly matters to me. This dark is dark enough for me. I do not wish to be seen but see.

(They say there are glass doors which prevent you from being seen even while you see everything!)

The quiet cajoles me into sleep. From sleep emerges rhythms that roll from the tongue. I get him hooked to the tongue. He struggles but can't get off the hook. This time I am the angler, he is the fish. I temper the rod. It is supple but solid. I hold it. I go fishing. He is the eye of the rod and whatever fish fall into the net, it is his net. Alas! I regard it as mine; guard it as mine only. And strangely it turns out to be his. Everything.

Dive deep!

Dive deep!

I hear the unsung song. In the deep you hear only unheard melodies. The rhythms of the song are unfamiliar. Rather, rhythms are familiar, the song I hardly heard before.

The Mother says:

"You see everything
that I show you;
and show them
to others who think
I didn't show them!"

"That's true, Mother! I am your window. Window insulates your power from giving a shock! They can enjoy it without fright, without fear, without fascination and addiction." But, even then. I murmur, you should lend your eyes, displace ours.

Quick! Say the eyes that are instantly displaced. I no longer see things that I ordinarily think I see. The eye is on fire when I see with "my" eyes. The eye is proof against that fire when he lends, loans his eyes to me. (He is willing, he says, to close the loan account and graft his eyes forever! Are you listening?) The third eye, they call it. It simply doesn't matter. Second or third, there is no eye at all in this seeing. When the seeing eye merges with the seeing, you get this eye.

Oh, *Ma*! What do you make me see! Do I deserve that? Even when he lends his eyes. Even when he says see through me. Even when he holds the angling rod from slipping from the hands? The soul-bewitching Mother is swaying her body in a rhythm that has no rhyme or reason in the body. Even with his eyes I am

frightened that I may go blind. Willing, joyous suspension of your
eye is what saves you from annihilation, I recall.

A side-glance from her, and
Hundreds run after her.
With old age dropped,
With garments shed,
With eyes blinded,
They run into the flame
Like moths!

Such, I see, is that intoxicating *maya* of the mother's form.
Enough to fix one forever on the tip of the sword of her
enchantment. I feel no urge to be a moth. I am her child. And as a
child I watch what he then shows:

Who is that? I can no longer see the mother. The mother
appears now in the garb of the Beloved. I seem to know. The face
is familiar. I can't say for certain. Yet it is a known face. A face
that crossed so many seas to emerge here.

The face and the form are radiant. No youthful flush; that is
only froth. Radiant with resilience that comes from crossing
swords with time. She is stretching her arms. I can hardly see the
Other. (The Other is always either Father or Mother). But should
one 'see' always. One can as well watch. I watch.

How joyously
The luminous
Twin twine
Each other?
It is not clinging
But warming
To each other.
It is not closing
In on each other,
For where are
The two?
I see no two forms.

Am I seeing right? I wonder. I puzzle but puzzled in a way that
does not puzzle and needle what I see. Puzzling that is piercing the
knots that blind the eye:

There is no
Abandonment here:
For there is
Nothing that one
Abandons oneself to;
There is only the
Moment that is
Never momentary.
The moment is
A miracle, for
The moment erects
Nothing; therefore,
Nothing that falls
No seed to fall
No ground to receive.
An endless moment
Of rendering the seed
Unto Her who is
The seed, the ground,
The plant and the fruit.
A dance that
Is a paradox,
For, all dance is
A paradox.

Normally quiet, he is quieter now. Half-closed eyes are sparkling with a glow that has no body to wear. Extinct is the flesh; extinguished the fire. The spine sings in sheer ecstasy. The serpent is electric. Touch it you get a shock that makes you take a leap—an instant leap—into the lotus. Shock that is a leap. Shock that does not shatter or make you shiver. But makes you shine in a way that you never saw your own body shine in that splendour!

Parama Premahamsa
Rahasya tantra
Is that what I see?

26

PIERCING WITH A PIECE OF GLASS

I increasingly need my sanity—more of it than what he seems to allow me to exercise. Every day brings revelations that engender re-visioning. Ordinary no longer holds me. In fact, I do not even know whether I can any longer think of the ordinary as normal. For the normal no more appears normal. Ordinary, you think. He suddenly becomes unusual in a split second. Unusual you decide and in a minute he appears frighteningly normal. The borderline seems to vanish. But he deliberately makes the borderline firmly appear again.

It is play of the most exquisitely crafty kind. Craft that makes you decide that he can never be just an innocent child. Innocent? You will be shocked when you are the butt of the pranks he plays, he perpetrates. I suspect he and mother are in collusion: "You play the game. I will see to it that nobody guesses it is your play." They seem to say to themselves.

Perfect he is. Yet he goes through the motions of practice. He can simply plunge and reach the depth and yet, he says, he learns swimming. Even if he tells you about what he does and did, don't be too sure that he means it. Normally he hides himself, his real self I mean. "*Gadadhar* Bhattacharya: that is what I am," he tells me. "But I know you only as...." "Ramakrishna? Right. It hardly matters. How you name me," he says.

Late in the day, witless, and therefore restless, I lie on the bare ground. For once, alone. I want to re-collect everything. Re-new everything. Not re-live, please. Just think and view everything. In quiet, in isolation on the grounds of Panchavati. In the darkness of the place. Darkness suits me—I said. "I am the One who keeps darkness dark, light light...." Oh my! Why this distraction again. Not after what I see.

Not after what he sees, says and shows. Anything that he sees he sees, just sees. Nothing more nothing less. The Mother is. Yes, it must be so: she is. That is enough for him. But tell him that beyond Mother there is a state that does not require your Mother to experience it. He is inclined to believe that. But even for what is beyond, for experiencing that Beyond, he requires Mother before—hand! To tell him "Go ahead! See what is beyond me. What is beyond me can only be what is before me," she says.

Not that seeing the Beyond is beyond him. Not that he cannot lose himself in the ocean; not that he cannot become sugar. But he wants to taste sugar. Deliberately he downgrades becoming; he wants to be and experience the many. "Keep me alert; don't drown me in bliss," he says to Mother. "Drown me in rasa but drag me out of that!" Strange attachment to *lila*. Incredible attachment to the world, with all its madness, its grief, its sorrow, its illusion. Play. That is what he likes.

That is what I like about him. No pedestal, no altar, no fetish. 'Be my chum' that is enough. Otherwise would I see those things that no human can see and survive? Experiences he gives are enough—one is enough—to shatter your being. His grace keeps you from running to a shrink. How many experiences that he throws before you, in profusion, with profound affection. "All these are for you! Have them either one or all. Whatever you like." Whatever I think of them, he says, "That suits me." The laugh that adorns the words never fades. Disarming laughter. But arming you with awareness, with alert attention—but those muscles and arms can be flexed only as he pleases and when he pleases.

Whenever I walk in the garden I get the feeling that I was here earlier. That I trod this ground, saw the Ganga, drew breath here, touched with sheer ecstasy. I hardly understand: it communicates without understanding. Every particle of dust whispers to me: "we were here together, dust particles at his lotus feet!" Every wave caresses me: "I held you in my arms for so long...." The wind whispers: "Don't you remember the fragrance we inhaled!"

Can such memory die? What seems to disappear is experience. Memory always is. Sometimes clouded; often clear. Experience is a dream. Memory is the reality.

The memory of that sharp spike between the eyebrows. How the needles needle me into the experience that is memory and memory that is experience! How I could withstand it is beyond me... even now.

"I am worried!" he tells me. Worry? For him to worry? "Yes, I have my worries, what do you think?" he reiterates. A sigh escapes him. That makes me start. Perhaps, this is real. Not play. The forehead is wrinkled, for a moment. For long that forehead cannot allow a wrinkle. It clears instantly.

"You know without the Mother I am not! And he wants me to forget her. Forget my mother? You can as well say, forget that I am!" (Which, of course, he does quite often.) I know who the 'he' is. A severe-looking monk stern, taciturn. No nonsense of *maya* and mother. Everything is an illusion, he says. I see this fellow closeted quite often with him. Perhaps, to my mentor he is the tormentor. He torments him with the idea: all that you go raving about as your mother is so much poppy cock. "Mother! Fancy1" he says, quite audibly, with disdain that makes me wince. I do not know how he receives it with such serenity bordering on acceptance of what this monk-chap says. (I don't have much use for this kind of monk.)

I see both of them closet themselves quite often. Must be he is instructing him. Something I hear: "*Brahma Satyam Jagat mithya.*" Not knowing these big words, I ask him. "The world is illusory; *Brahman* alone is real." I need not have bothered to know. It hardly helps me. My world is real: for it contains my beloved and anything that has one like him is real, must be real! "You don't understand," he says, "this is the highest philosophy, the top rung of the ladder."

If this is philosophy, and this is the top rung I feel like doing without it. "Does the top rung being reached permit reentry into your ladder? I ask. "No, it doesn't. once you reach, you dissolve, merge forever. And where is the question of coming back to me and to mother? You stay there." Even before he completes the sentence I nearly shout, "Not for me!"

"We are not talking about you! You fool! I am worried for myself. How to climb and then climb down. I don't know how this could be. Suppose I forget mother, staying there? That would be death, real death, if you know what I mean." 'If' saves me. I do not know what he means. 'If' is real for me and that is I consign it to '*Brahman*'. My attitude is that of a simpleton:

Ramprasad's songs,
A jug of her wine,
And he beside me
Enough unto the last!

"You seem always to get lost! Can't you listen!" he almost scolds me. This time it is I who smile. That is the limit: it infuriates him. "Will you wipe that idiomatic smile off your face?" he really is angry. (Of course, he meant idiotic!) I don't know why: I now roar with laughter. Uncontrollable, irresistible. He is puzzled, peers into my eyes. And a smile spreads across his face: the infection is caught. He chuckles, visibly controlling the felt fun inside.

"I am worried," he repeats. And there it rests. We decide to sit on the banks. I looking at him; he looking at the river. The temple seems out of range, just out of reach, twilight closes in on us. An hour that always mesmerises me. In twilight I see him brighter. In light I see him less. I am being honest: this is true. The hour that brings Gopala back home with his herd. The hour that awakens the fragrant dust of earth with the cattle trotting on it.

Who keeps watch of time in such twilight. Its limpid flow is magical. One just floats like a dry, dead leaf, a petal of the huge lotus. Drifting with the lotus as one of its petals is fun, real fun. But you should decide: whether to be one of the petals or the lotus itself. For one, I want to remain a petal! You can be with others. With him.

The lights in the temple do not come this far. They seem to know his requirements. Quiet and darkness. If it is unrelieved

darkness it is all the better. The dark speaks to the depths. And the
depths reveal the Wild Woman and the Wilder Womb: the cosmos
cannot contain them; the universe is not space enough for them.
Instinctively eyes close in adoration:

"Thou art Mother,
The river beneath the river,
The light from the abyss
The wolf woman,
The bone woman,
The Wolverine,
You are of the woods;
Thou art the Spider Woman
Weaving the fate
Of humans and animals
And plants and trees
And rocks and ravines,
Of rivers and waterfalls.
You are Dhumavati,
The Mist-Mother
Who brings all light
To consciousness;
Thou art Dakini
The clear-seeing one
Who sees everything.
Thou art even
The Goddess of Obscenity,
With bawdry for head
And eyes all over!"

I intone and merge into the dance of the river. I even go into
the hollows that hold the breath by their sheer beauty. Suddenly a
whisper comes: "Don't be the salt doll for some time. Or you
cannot see what happens now!" Should I care? With him, with me,
beside me? I look at him and he isn't there! He disappears just like
that. I know it. Quite often it happens. And I like it. I even love it.
Re-visioning is just not there without losing. As much I want to
gain, so much I want to lose. Loose your hold and s/he holds you
close, so close that the closeness is nonexistent.

It is good I lose him. Or else how will I search for him? I look all over. In familiar corners; in known spaces. In trodden paths with the stars above showing the way. With the birds—strangely awake—holding their breath lest I get distracted. The trees sway: "Bravo! Move on!" the leaves love it. They whisper to each other: "So close to him and yet so far. He is like us: we are the tree. Then why look for it!"

I do look for him. And find him. About to draw near, I stop in my tracks. That *advaiti* is with him. Whispering something; cajoling, rather. "You can do this;" he seems to whisper, this time, somewhat fiercely, I think, "you are on the threshold: just one jump and you are in! Take that final leap! Cut everything that stands in the way. Take the shears: Mow down the grass. Clear the way. Everything must go. Come on!"

My Beloved is always like that. Tender, frail delicate. (Or so he seems). "I can dissolve everything but not...." The naked one completes: "not your mother? Right?" He nods. Grateful that he need not spell out the Mother (who, by the way, can spell her?) "Specially your mother! You must cut her, cleave her, in any case she is Chinnamasta." Did I hear slight derision in the tone? I'm not sure.

He looks as helpless as ever. Dissolve Mother while she is the Great Dissolver! Who can wield a sword against her? She holds and wields all the swords. It's just unthinkable. *Mantra*, I can forget; *tantra*, I can throw off; *yantra*, I don't need. But Mother? That is different!

I hide myself
In Thy bosom;
I gaze at Thy face
And cry out: "Mother! Mother!"
I sink in the Sea of Bliss
And lose myself in
That sea of yours
And to cleave Thy
Face? The Bewitching,
Benumbing Face,

The Face that fashions
All the faces!
The *advaiti* is furious. For a man who rejects illusion, to get so angry amuses me. Perhaps part of Mother's delusion. He is looking for something. In the dark, I cannot see. (In retrospect it is good that I did not see.) And think (wrongly) I do not care. I see his blissful face now creased with worry. That is all I see and all that I need to see. But something glints in the dark. Is it a piece of broken glass? Or something else that I can not see and make out?

With steps that are firm, face that is beaming, eyes that are set, the advaiti approaches him. Oh, my! In a split second, in a flash of lightning, like light, he pierces the piece of glass (I now see clearly) into the middle of his eyebrows!

I am frozen with pain. That body is stunned. Instinctively I cry: "How dare you do that to...." I can't finish. The shock waves engulf me. And I swoon.

"What is the matter? Haven't you taken food? You swoon like this!" he is whispering into my ears. And gently applying ash-*vibhuti,* in the middle of my eyebrows. "That should make you strong!" he declares.

Ganga flows gently.

27

NO JOURNEY FOR THE PIOUS

He again slips away. Where I do not know. I do not even wish to. Perhaps, he goes to the deep forests to relax. By the side of roaring waterfalls he could be. Enjoying the fall and ruminating on our Fall that is strictly unnecessary. Whereabouts are not known. Perhaps, if you enquire of those who know, you may know. You, too. But I have no impulse.

The impulse is scorched. Ever since I saw him, here, there, everywhere. His limited frames I used to like. Now I enjoy everything. And I deliberately go out to enjoy everything. The boat is full of those faces of hers which haunt me. So radiant they are: so wretched they appear. That is what bothered me earlier. Now it does not. In fact, nothing bothers me.

That small child sitting in the corner. Frightened beyond her wits. Sunken eyes, skin that lost its pallor; hair matted, neglected. None to comb this mother's lovely locks. And how hungry she appears! Eyeing everywhere. Is there a grain to gobble up? If mother can take the form of hunger, here she is: *annagatha prana* with no Annapurna to feed her. To take her into her lap and feed her.

Amazing it is. The Mother's maze: that is what is amazing. Is she perverse, cruel, torturing with known tools of torture: hunger, the foremost. Is she fond of human blood? Then there is no blood even left in some. For her to suck with relish.

Child I thought. I have to think twice. Perhaps I haven't seen properly. Sight is blurred... I have to see twice. Learn to see twice.

Things get out of focus if seeing twice is not cultivated. I cultivate
diligently but I forget, too, equally diligently. Otherwise, how
could I not see that child in the corner. She is, sure, child of the
mother. But she could be as well a replica of the mother's womb.
She is grown-up for a man. No child in that sense. Replica? No,
rather a mirror.

    Oh, mother!
    This mirror
    Is a clean one;
    It gives thy
    Pure reflection
    But reflection
    Meshed in
    Thy *maya*!
    You sport
    In the mirror, too.

Transposed! The child-woman teases me. I look at her and
seem to know her.... Yes, I see her quite clearly; no haze hangs
over my eyes. I nurse the seed, the seed sown in memory. I watch
its flowing forth. I watch with fearful enjoyment. Oh, *Ma*! To what
depths one is made to go when once s/he is mad after you! You
unhinge the one who starts to settle in you.

What agony they go through! They? Why do I exclude
myself? I do not. They all are myself. I am in those haunted ones,
the hushed ones; hushed by your guardians, *Ma*! Hounded out,
dispossessed, driven from their abode, totally driven. Victims of
the taboos of the terror that those taboos unleash. All your villains
seem to be let loose! They catch these *abhaginis*, catch them with
the noose that they claim is your noose. The noose that nullifies all
that does not seem proper.

I enjoy all this; I must say only the noose I want removed from
your throat, too. Abandon oneself to whatever one seeks you with,
Mother. The most grotesque is glorious, if only you are the
gorgeous one that is sought after. The most bizarre is beautiful.
What is beauty except what is bizarre? You are yourself with your
tongue hanging from your mouth in bashfulness bizarre! Many

swoon even at the very sight. You are the warrant for everything, the wanton, the vicious, the virtuous, the self-righteous.

Love for you does strange things, don't you know? No lengths, to which they do not go, to nurse that seed in their womb. Ask them to go naked; naked they will be. Ask them to touch their nose with the tip of the tongue, they willingly do. Ask them to lie upside down, they lovingly do. Order them to draw back their seed; joyously, radiantly, relishing it, they withdraw. They relish but do not relapse. Ask them to take your sword and kill themselves, joyously they do. (For, they very well know, in your lap there's no one to kill, no one is killed.)

All because of love. If nothing else, I can vouch for at least this. I roam[ed] all over, panicking that you left, you withdrew from my gaze. I weep unseen, unknown, weep, weep for you. Tears that are enough to salt the oceans. Burning tears, scorching the body, wasting it away, so that even the body is not seen. And I want you as my lover. I want you as my *parakiya*.

I am demented. Otherwise how can I think of actually holding you in my arms? I do not think even. I want to hold. No thinking, only wanting; wanting for ages past, for ages to come. For hours that are. That woman-child, child-woman, there in the corner of the boat, blinking at everyone who looks at her. She I am. Who else can it be. She has stepped into my shoes. I claim them now. She willingly gives them. I get off the boat and manage to get on to the banks of the river. I don't even know whether I have clothes. (Does it matter? The matter, with clothes is that they are matter! And hence, do not matter.)

It, sure, is a jungle. The banks deceive. The lush jungle they conceal from the prurient and the puritan. I only have eyes for it. And only one face they 'eye':

She wears a garland of skulls
And holds the head of a man;
From the skull-garland
Fall drops of blood
On to her limbs
Covered by the red sandal paste.

I am in a trance when I see
The forehead marked
with the vermilion of love,
the igniter of
the Light of Wisdom.

That light is what lights up my path. I move silently. I now
realise: he is surrounded. By devotees. I must go stealthily. Lovers
of mother, I am told, are *kumathihi*, devious-minded. That suits
me. I am one. Lovers are devious: devotees are so dedicated that
the devious leave them behind. I am devious and stealthy. That
image of the helpless child in a corner of the boat I consign-
consent to sign-to Ganga. Let her keep it in trust. When I emerge
from my tryst I may need it again. Perhaps, the loved one sent
word around.

The trees do not breathe;
The birds stop from snoring;
The animals are alert
To watch the fun;
The forest is on fire
And yet they do not flee.
This forest-fire is so much fun!

After what travail I reach the forest! So devoted they are, they
are intent on catching me. Even here in the forest. "Catch her and
throw her into the prison. Let the police look after her (knowing
what the police, looking, after is, they smirk with satisfaction)."
But I am sly I escape and land here. I comb the forest. (Even comb
my hair, you know!) The stars peep through the leaves of the huge
trees; the leaves gladly yield enough space to light the small way I
need to reach him.

Now I remember: even the river plays tricks. I do not seem to
enjoy her favour. I get the impression that she advances to drown
the boat. This is an impression; but my invoking my mother, Tara,
to quell the waves and quieten my fear is not:

Oh mother!
On my way
To the beloved,

I cross this
Lake of nectar
By the boat
Plied by your saktis!
Let thy sheer sheen
Silence the surging
Waves!

Waves quiet, leaves filter enough light and Tara herself rows me across. Lands me on the bank. But where is he? Can I locate him in such a huge *manasavana*? The mind forest? Infested with weeds. So many. How can I—on my own—hope to pull them out? (Weeds are reincarnate forms of the pious, preventing ones who guard the Beloved!)

Painful the journey is;
With piety all around
Protecting you from
My arms, pain is
More of a pain
Than it actually is!

All over I search. I stumble often. But I rise. Often rise only to fall again. Where do they hide him so carefully? Is he sick and needs their care and concern. But do they know why he is sick? Sick for me! Pining for me! Located but again lost, I am—I am the one he is sick for. Unless he is sick would you go see him? (Of course, I do ill or well.)

His sickness is a ruse. To rouse you from your long slumber.

I am lost in a reverie. Reverie is the only thing that you relish when the effulgent, radiant Presence is yet to en-vision your being. But reverie refuses to remain reverie. The serpent hisses loud and strong. But sound that is not heard, strength that is not felt. My helplessness stares me in the face. How faceless I am!

I am no Radha
For friends to anoint
My burning body
With serene, sandal-wood paste!
Unable to reclaim

Or revive me
The maids of Radha
Weep!
I am thirsty, too. Not the thirst I feel anything can quench;
except a secret course in miracles. ('Ramana' he once called it.)
The miracle that, if few perform, fewer experience. It is a course
in formative and performative breath! Good. But where is the
performer-enchanter? (Closeted with the Enchantress?)

Fishermen dragging the Big, the Only Fish that they want
desperately to catch, he tells me. That is what loving him is. "Open
your mouth," he says "touching...

Open your mouth
Touching heaven
And the nether world
With your jaws
And utter the
Name: "Beloved"

He says many things which I occasional, recall: where is space
for anything else when he occupies all that is available? That is
why occasionally remembrance of words and things past; constant
communion where words and things are lost. That is the state. But
then, where is he? 'In your heart?' you say. Yes. Since I lost it,
where is that? Has he succumbed to the wiles of his wayward
disciples? Remaining there imprisoned by the shackles of *sadhana*
that is drained of *prema* (*prema* of my, of any, kind)?

The heart is now reaching the head. Even Tara cannot stop the
onrush. I flush with anger at this hiding. Even the nonchalance I
learn from him (since mother arranges everything, be nonchalant,
he says) is now eclipsed. I now know the power of anger of this
kind. I gather all the strength (that s/he herself gives); I flex my
muscles (s/he gives herself, those too.) My eyes are fiery balls.
Since he himself tells the tale and technique I open my mouth:

No letting go, this time.
I shall devour you!
I have no other path.
Leave it to you?

No, not this time.
Not at all.
I shall taste you.
Relish you, that
Is how I shall devour you.
I forsake you and
Go to my Kali for your sake!
Kali blackens my hands;
My face, all my limbs
In my already black body.
In that blackness
That darkens darkness itself
I shall devour you!
Seething anger surges in me. I no longer care. Care for what I
say. Care for what I do. He has troubled me enough. Teased me. I
tolerated. Not this time. Helplessness and anger! Strange *Sakti-
Siva sangama*! Anger at what he reduces me to:
You cause so much
Agony! Short of
Devouring you
There is hardly a way!
Who knows what you
Are up to even now!
With that dazzling smile
You deceive many;
I am not going
To be among those many!
Be sure: I would
Rather go from door to door
Warning against your wiles
Than fall into your arms
Calling you...
"Then whose arms are seeking you? Not mine?" I gape (as I
tell you so many times) like a stupid scorpion-bitten monkey. Oh
Ma! Have I all along been here only? In his arms? Securely?
Safely? Snugly?

The sparkling teeth scintillate in the night. (The pious ones vanish. No one is around!)

She who loves the battle,
She who loves her *lila*.
She who is the actor,
The director,
Everything,
Whose beauty radiates
The light of love

smiles and tucks me into his lap and ties me up with her string, this kite still held in her hands.

28

THE POISONOUS ROD THAT PIERCES

I sleep on the verandah for the night. To sleep anywhere in that *lilakshetra* is intoxicating; strangely bracing. It revives you, rejuvenates you. Charges you with a zest you hardly think you have. The drooping and drowsy spine is erect. Energy flows, flooding the body (and all that goes with it) with a strange glow. Even my body. That is what is puzzling. Even I feel the charge. The entire *lilakshetra* seems cordoned off from all negatives. (If one can think of negatives at all!)

And that cordoning and communing extends to everyone, to every object in that magnetic field. I look at the horses that draw the carriage he travels in. How lucky they are! They pull with their energy the One who pulls all to himself. I feel as if the horses do not simply run; they jump with joy, indeed, float like foam on the road, their feet hardly touching the ground. I prostrate to them and the Ashwapati who consents to be drawn by them.

And the boatmen? They seem to know. Guileless, trusting, faith coursing through their veins, they vie with each other to draw him to their boat. Of course, they are there even earlier, sometimes the boatmen know or, perhaps, do not know. They rowed him across earlier when he went to the forests at the behest of his father. How buoyant they all were! To get the touch of the hallowed feet on their boats! Something that *punya* alone brings. And they also remember what they ask and the assurance that he gives: "When you come to that shore of that river, I shall row you all across! Nothing to worry!"

And Ganga? When he touches her and sprinkles a few drops of her water on his head, she is overjoyed. Her entire body shivers in ecstasy of that tenderness that marks all that he touches. Himself stainlessly pure, taking the water of Ganga to sprinkle on himself! Sight for the gods, and for humans who could be gods. I do not see anyone else who sees Gangamayi as he does. Sanctity and tenderness strangely mingle in that glance.

Tuning my entire being to all that I see, I rest on the verandah; until the call comes for me from him. I do not wait with anxiety for the call. I relax and wait. I have infinity behind and eternity before me. After seeing what I see, seeing can only be eternal. That seeing has no frontiers, no thresholds, no time-charts, no *panchangas*, almanacs.

"How many things Mother shows me and I wish to show you. But can I?" he asks. "Why not?" If you love us show us everything that you see. Make us see everything that you show, you may not allow us to see. Perhaps, that is as it ought to be. If he does not tend towards pre-tending, our pretense to omniscience, the bluff is called. "I show everything. Nothing is concealed," he says.

"But you both show and take precautions that we do not see, am I right?" I ask. "Yes and no!" he replies. And nothing else is spoken. I look across the courtyard and get up from the verandah. I come alive instantly. Alert to his Presence in the adjacent room. To be adjacent to him is to breathe in the fragrance, the scent as it were, that emanates from his body. There is something indescribable about the scent that travels from him. For a long time I wonder what is unique about that fragrance. Loosing childhood long ago, how can I expect to guess the fragrance of this child of Kali! The mouth emits strange betel-nut smell: I forget I offer him myself in adoration:

> beloved!
> These betel nuts,
> Culled from vines
> That creep like a snake;
> Are luminous and lovely
> Reflecting your *soundarya*.

Blended with cardomom-powder
They freshen your
Mouth that, drinking
Blood, needs this flavour
—for us to near you,
to reach your lap.

I offer them with my own breath feeling the chewing of the betel-nut! Isn't it I who enjoy the scented nut? (Being a nut, myself, I do require it.) He is still inside the room. I want him in the open. Out in the wilds: there he is the Wild Woman. I like that. I crave for it. I crave for him to roam wildly in nature without anything to restrain, anything to confine.

Only in the wild can I grab him. Hold him close. Not allow him any freedom to free himself from my grip. I angled and angled for ages that I know, and years that I both know and know not. Sits before me! I can't recognise! Sits in full form and seeing is prevented. Strange it sounds, doesn't it? Yes, it is strange. He wants it that way. So be it. I say. "I am not in a hurry!" I even tell him. He smiles. "If you come down, yourself, for all of us, again and again, then why should I get cooped 'up' there?" I ask him.

He doesn't come out of the room. Perhaps, someone else, too, is holding him up. He likes it that way. Let him. I am the last one to hold anything against his others. I slip away from the verandah. The vast expanse all around beckons me. Horses that draw his carriage neigh: "Go out child! How can he not be with you! Go out!" No one seems to notice me and that is fine. Getting noticed- I learnt long ago from him—is a nuisance. Noticing too often leads to being notorious. I do not want to be. I am the secret one. I enjoy those secrets. For my eyes only. (And how he yields in secret! Unimaginable! And leave it to the unperceived realm.)

I roam everywhere. The bird in the sky has everywhere to go. Sky is the limit. I roam and peep into the passages that he rarely permits people to see. Not that he doesn't want them to see. But that they cannot see and therefore cruel to expose them to what they cannot see, congenital blindness, I call it. (the genital-confined myopia and grogginess). Vultures only see carrion. But carrion is burnt by the sun, reduced to ashes, to dust. And we return to the dust.

The dust of Dakshineswar. And I roll in it, on it; contented, carefree. I do what I like there. Under his observant but affectionate eye. He rarely prohibits anything to be used as fuel for faith. Enjoy anything but don't lose sight of the mother. If she is in sight everything is in harmony. All objects and experiences fall into patterns. You enjoy in a way that does not leave a bitter taste- of exhaustion, of dissipation, of enervation.

I can not say I follow what he says. Of late I notice another kink in 'my' mind. I do not get worried if, I do not follow. I wait. Either he will explain or a context comes when what he says becomes what he shows. I oscillate between warp and woof-of listening to and looking at things he says and shows. And he has another trick in his bag of surprises.

How shall I put it? Let me try if I can. The trick is to make you some sort of expert in words and, to show it off, impel you towards a context. Context in which saying things well is considered as doing those things wisely. Then what you consider your competence becomes a crooked noose round your neck. Since ideas and words come easily, you are impressed, yourself, first of all. And that is the beginning, of the fall. The words are made to turn round and laugh at you! Laugh with disdain, with derision. "At least we were safe in the dictionary. When you bring us out, and show us to others how great we are, then we realise that our greatness is proclaimed by a person who knows not how to match meaning and word, marry us to reality! And we naturally feel chagrined. Out of that chagrin is born our disdain," say the words, out in the cold, shivering without the protecting sheets of their own being.

"You must learn to be silent," he says. "Learn," he repeats. I do listen. But is listening learning? Grandly I proclaim, pontificating I claim all words are her *matrikas*. He listens amused. And you are caught in a maze. What is amusing is meant for musing. I play on words and forget his play. Until he hits gently. A firm but gentle tap on the head. The head clears and you breathe again. freedom from suffocation. Exalting and exulting, exhilarating. (Can I get rid, at any time, of my addiction to assonance, to alliteration? Assuming what they are really?)

How intimate he can be! But intimacy that has its own interior checks and balances. Beyond a point he does not allow you to pry into his secrets. That is only for him and the mother. Perhaps, the secrets are not secrets at all. They are so because for you everything should be open: not even the suggestive jargon of the grocer to make you buy should be there. Everything on the plate, naked, quivering in its nakedness. Seen by all, shown for all....

Amusing myself with my musings, I sit on the banks of the pond. It is in the house near the banks of this pond that he assumed form. Consented to come to those who cognise his coming. That's why the bank (Gattu we call it) is so important for me. Tired of resting on the ocean he consents to come to the shore, the gattu, the threshold that makes the ocean stick to its bound-and allows him to sport on the banks, play his drama! How many are enchanted by his coming to the banks! Specially those who have yet to learn swimming in the ocean, like the fish!

I am not sure where he is at the moment. He waves and wafts away like wind. (Leaving himself behind strangely felt Presence, startlingly soothing.) I sit with my fishing rod. With the bait hidden; and the bait hiding poison inside. The fish touch and die instantly. The *jalpushp* wither, blasted in a second. So fatal is the hidden poison. And the harpoon-like rod pierces through them. They are thrown into my basket, bleeding from the blood so bled.

I am ecstatic. So many caught so many shedding their blood for me-a shedding that doesn't appear to me as something I should not! Fish are meant to be caught, cooked and relished. In fact, I admire *tantra* since it has *matsya* as an ingredient on its menu. (Of course, I am a vegetarian *tantric*. Fish is fishy for me.) So full of joy I sing (if you can call it that!)

The central canal
Is fed by the
Two streams;
Overflowing, the

Centre of my being
Flooded by the
Engulfing waves
I swim joyfully!
I am the fish!

I sport with the sport of angling. For, I sport to feed him the fish that I catch. How he relishes fish caught by me! How many queer fish he knows and how many recipes of cooking. The ripe ones receive special dressing and extra attention. The unripe ones are kept waiting. They don't mind. They do not even know that someone is waiting there to dress them, skin them and cook them. But all sooner or later get cooked. That you can be sure of.

I notice: others do not catch as much as I do. They do not have baits. They keep away from poison-tipped rods. I use the trick exclusively. Am I not special? His special supplier of fish? I gloat in visions of visible appreciation of my heroic angling. I laugh in my sleeve. How naive these folks can be! The natural way of fishing? Two hoots for that! I want my way. Am I a *Pundit* for nothing? I bring my *punditry* to catch them. And they get caught. They dare not move away.

Enough, I decide. And thinking of the canal that sings, I stand a basket of fish on my head. Ready to move to where the cooking is to be done. I stroll along without a trace of anything, of any emotion in the mind. I must have achieved *bhava-samadhi*, even *savitarka, sahaja samadhi*. "If fish could induce this, let me catch more!" I merrily say this to myself.

I hardly take a step, he seems heading towards me. The face appears unfamiliar. An unfamiliar pain is visible on the face. Pain, it seems, intentionally inflicted by someone. The placid face is still placid but with a new paint of pain I do not seem to have seen earlier. It is puzzling. Puzzling enough to result in panicking. Panic makes adoration rush back with a pang of memory.

Oh, Mother!
Let the effulgent
Fire of perception
Force itself

Into me, this
Pot made of thy clay,
And provide nourishment.
Let its flame
Blaze forth in
Thousand tongues
And leave me
Spotlessly pure
In thy love and strength.
So that I know what is
To be known.

He smiles: faint but fair enough. I gather my wits, scattered
grain picked up by the still fingers. I draw near, almost tempted to
hold him. The emotion refuses to act. *Iccha, jnana* do not wish to
change themselves and become *kriya*. I gulp and gape. I hasten-
that much I do and gaze witless. Do I hear some words. True, he
seems to be intoning something (to himself, it seems):

All and everything
You are, Mother.
Singer, song, singing
You are all that is.
The rhythm of your
Being is the
Rhythm of your
Srishti, shitthi, laya.
The rhythm pierces
Without pricking;
Anglers without harming
Catch fish like that
And they cry in ecsatsy!
Willingly they jump
Into your net!
Know the rhythm
That rules everything
And I know I can
Rule over you!

Even as he sings blood trickles from the mouth. Barely visible in the darkness that, now, stifles me. But blood can be easily seen- if you are used to it.

Why should he intone anything now, let alone sing? Now, specially, when I know he is sick. (with the sickness of all beings). He should restrain his *bhava*. That is what the physician says (but does the magician and the musician listen?)

"Why should you come out in the cold, now? And aggravate the throat, already sensitive?" I ask him almost (with 'righteous') anger. Anger does not last. Fear overtakes, reverent fear. A glance at that face that registers pain and helpless anger. That the one who thinks he is learned has not learnt the lesson of rhythm. "You fool!" Mother intones in my ear:

the poisonous rod that
pierces through the
mouth of the fish
rushes their
shed blood
to his mouth!
can he help bleeding!

Fear paralyses me. Words are frozen. They refuse to rescue me. The fish laugh in glee. "Let this chap learn: there is still time...." And I thought I achieved *bhava samadhi*!

29

THE STILL CENTRE OF THE POLE

Unless you are
passionate,
you cannot know the
Paramahamsa, the
Passionless One!

"How clever you are!" he nods his head. I think in appreciation. But one cannot be sure. The Passionless One is beyond passion-poetry. He is caught but does not remain there. Through the mist of poetry, he rarely misses the person behind and before, around and above but not in the poetry. Poetry is the illusion. Person is the reality, he seems to be saying. (Or, I seem to like hearing something like this!)

"You know something?" I perk my ears. Whenever he says, "You know," the idea is "You better listen. You do not know." So I listen. "I would roam in the Mother's *kshetra* with a bamboo pole on my shoulders. Balancing it is easy if you know...," he leaves it there. I do not press for completion. Completion and the anxiety for it are just that: anxiety. Anxiety never makes for completion— of anything. "Consciousness wriggles about even in fish..." he breaks the silence and adds. "Since you seem to like fish, I thought that should be helpful!" Who told him I like fish? I am a total vegetarian, for all I know now. I pursue the pole, however. I also must take, his pole on my shoulders. Mine are too frail, I know. But once I start trying, the pole may yield. "You must be silly, how can you bear her pole?" he asks.

That question I can answer. I am clever like Ganesha, her son.
He teaches me (in secret!) "Go round the pole and you have gone
round the Prithvi Mata, the Earth Mother!" I laugh with sheer
exultation! Of wresting the secret. *Pradikshna* I can do; *dakshina*,
I have already given: bond-slave bound by his/her love! That is
that. In inexpressible joy, I shoot my eyes down and wear the
glasses he gives and sing:

'Sri Ram'akrishna!
Paramahamsa!
Thou art the
Mystic
Pole—Centre
Round which revolves
The Prithvi Mata,
The Earth Mother.
Thou art the hole
In the centre of
The jade—disk,
The hole that contains
The whole Being
Of Earth and Heaven
Matter undergoes
 Metamorphosis:
Far beyond all being
And becoming,
Thou art the
Unmoving mover,
The *Achala* that
Is *Chala*.
At the heart of
Thy Pole
Is the raging Fire!
The Fire that burns
And begets and
Begets only to burn!

I feel I am able to understand the pole. Among the strange
things he does, this is one. Not more intriguing than his madness

itself. And the pole mystifies only those who are caught in polarities. Caught without the art of balancing. The art of yoking things together, the art that nature creates the illusion is just art. That is the illusion that Mother constantly uses to refract. So that, you are caught in the *maya*-box: you close it without any connecting door to other things.

I myself feel exhausted and emptied of everything that makes for connection. Where is the door that connects? Is there a door at all? Or, are we in a room without an exit, closed from all sides, deliberately cordoned off?

Strange ideas float in the mind. (to the extent that it allows such floating!) Ideas that I hardly try to regulate or even register firmly. I allow them to float on their own without any help from 'me'. Let him do whatever he likes and likes to since mother, too, likes them to be done. I have no intention of interfering with the movement of the serpent. If it wishes to jump, trot, crawl or creep, or even lie totally exhausted—that is her lookout. I have neither out-look nor look-out: all seem OK as things stand now.

Strange ideas? Strange vision and re-visions. I keep the glasses and they are not even polished. If they obstruct seeing, so be it. If they show with clarity, let that, too, be. The body registers, ever so mildly but clearly, the impact. Perhaps, the body has no business in this business of the dream-body, the, even, non-body. Extremes rack the frame. Quiet one day the body rouses itself from that quiet and upsets, on its own, everything that you wanted to achieve. Everything that you felt you wished to connect yourself with.

The *mandala* of darkness has, of course, its kendra bindu, the central point. But I do not wish to concentrate on that. I realise that to focus on a bindu is to shut oneself in without a door. But then there may be no prakarams or gates or doors. May be or may not be—the doorless could be the reality. And why speculate (unless speculation is also a spectacle!)? Not speculating but waiting and watching is the door—if you want the door not as a door but as a sign.

I wait and watch, watch and wait. Keeping everything empty. The Void, the emptiness is strangely soothing. I feel I lie on the waves even when the darkness threatens to smother me. But are children of the Dark One taken in by darkness? I hardly know. Perhaps yes, perhaps no.

All the time he watches me and I envision him. Obviously my physical sight is too inadequate to see him. But absence of adequacy in the physical is the generation of the inner view. I see him thus and I follow him wherever he goes, wherever he permits. He does not allow you everywhere. Whenever he knows that you have mere curiosity and not communion as your propelling force, curiosity which he often tells me is the spring board of *kamini-kanchana*. So that everything interior is reduced to *kamini* or *kanchana*. "The secret becomes the sordid," he tells me. And the sordid is always desire. Rather the sordid assumes the respectable form of a 'secret'. Since all secrets are of great interest to vultures looking for carrion, the secret gets decoded in terms of the carnal.

Ruminations come to an abrupt halt. He beckons to me. Keep silent, the beckoning says. Keep mum and watch me and mother. Just watch these watchless moments now. (Plenty of time for ruminations later.) Now is forever, and the secret is for all time to come. For all the curious to gaze at, the devout to delight in and the seeker to soak himself/herself in.

How intoxicated he appears now! The easy familiarity of only a few minutes earlier dissolves. The splendour that envelops him makes entry into that nearly impossible. The effulgence is electrifying but impenetrable. A thick, very thick glass case seems to emerge and enfold him. (The glass case?) You can see but cannot touch or even approach. He has this habit of conjuring in a split second something that even while within view decisively separates him from you. But he may still want you to be around: compassion is the key to your entry. And love more than compassion.

Through the glass darkly I see him enter a wood. A vast landscape of trees, specially of pine trees. The woods of Mother-*sakshatkara*, of *darshana*, of the Paramahamsa you can call them. The wood he enters stings me like a bee. The adoration "*kadambavanasini*" instinctively gets intoned. I realise fecundity oozing from the wood. He enters and I in adoration fall to the ground and evoke her Presence.

O Mother
The Dweller of this *vana*!
The magic of burnt wood,
The Creatrix,
Is there, I see,
In the burnt ashes.
Cremation and creation
Are the *ida* and *pingala*
Of Thy *Sushumna*,
And the wood rejoices
To be that!
And you sport
Here in the forest,
Trampling the mad-elephant
Of my mind with your very glance!

Does he need my evocation. It is my need, not his. I need it desperately. Need to enter the wood. Unless I propitiate her I cannot dare to even think of entering the wood.

See with what graceful steps he walks into the woods. As if expected and awaited. (Remove 'as if' then you come near the truth.) That he knows his way around, I can see. Every inch of the ground, every cranny. So light and elegant the footfalls. They echo in the heart as the rhythm that rocks the universe in her cradle. The feet that Brahma himself washed reverently, (with reverent fear!) And the feet take him to that grove of the pine-trees that is secluded. (And all groves and all trees are, for me, Panchavati. This is the original. They are replicas. For me, note!)

The pine must have seen enactments like this spread over aeons and aeons! Enactments by men (and women) mad after the mother. This is the evergreen tree of madness, the interior *upavana* of immortality. Green it was, it will be and it is. Green and fertile, the pine-trees pause in their breathing as the Paramahamsa places himself under them and instantly loses himself in her lap.

How unmoving he sits,

Under the trees,
Unmoving but mobile
In mother's womb!
Playing with her
Even while sitting
Nearly immobile.

Not given to being stable, I move around, seeing everything
through the glass. But is seeing the same as before? I suddenly
develop doubts. What he is doing now puzzles me. Puzzles and
nearly petrifies me. He is no longer sitting with eyes closed.
Seeing something his eyes bulge. What they see that so much
astonishes them, I cannot guess. But an earlier clue he let out
springs to the mind.

Remove the green scum
From the face of the lake.
You can then drink pure water.
The scum is quite thick
And impenetrable:
But *maya* bows in reverence
When the Mother/Master
Allow the scum to be
Removed!

That is what I try doing. Remove some of the scum. I can
hardly do it enough. It gathers again easily. I try desperately and a
door opens. My door to him opens. And a strange paradox greets
me. He is himself at it: trying to open a hidden door.... Is he
uttering something? I crane my neck and perk my ears:

Dvaraka
Thou who act
As Portress!

Is it my fancy? Could be. But I like it that way. Inbred,
difficult-to-give-up laws of association, *samskaras*, make me hear
it. And, of course, the city of nine gates constantly recurs. But
which gate? Should I ask that question?

All doors lead
To her!

The walls and
The doors are inseparable!
The temple door
Leads to the
Altar alone.
What sacrificial rites the door leads to! How could one guess?
One guesses from only the door one knows. (And many, he tells
me, are familiar with toilet doors. Even that is a door, yes, he says,
but dirt and garbage may cling to you. I now recall: he once called
it the "faeces door to female analysis"! whatever that means.)
Sovereign, wide,
Good, many and
Manifold are
The doors to
The ritual sacrifice,
The gods enter
Through doors
That are no doors
They are apertures
That the serpent delights to traverse
Through!
The movements
Move the rain
To shower pearls
That, like the home bird,
Rise up even as they seem to fall.
I hardly know why I write like this, and what they mean. I do
not even know whether, immersed in opening the hidden door, he
even hears it. But I do recall something he says quite often: "Of
late, kids are very intelligent! They seem to delight in turning
mother's *varnamala*, garland of words, her *matrikas*, upside
down. So *linga* is only that for them. Poor Siva is amazed that they
tug at him!" I am filled with, again fear. Am I, too, guilty?
I cease to get sunk in reveries. Instead, I swim joyfully
immersing myself in his luminous Presence. The Presence that
tries—again and again—to pierce through the hidden door.
Fascination overcomes fear. Fascination, in its turn, leads to

freedom from reveries that run riot... reveries that are heady but heretical; musings that titillate but do nothing much to jaded nerves. (Of late, scholar-kids have terribly jaded nerves that need a shot in the toilet!) That idea unnerves me. Am I heretical in covering everything with my own addictive patterns? Am I merely finding in his Presence a compensation for my erotic longings? Is, after all, spirituality merely heightened eros? And nothing else? Are frustrated emotional longings projected on to a Presence and through that projection-imagination the frustrations neutralised if not burnt totally? Ready to spring again into play when a stimulus presents itself?

I swim joyfully in the Presence. But the swimming does not stop these *chittavrittis*; these waves that rise and fall, fall and rise and roll me along. With strength that the very floating gives I cling to the Presence. This anchor is sheet-anchor against everything. Everything that troubles me, anything that tempts me. All these too, I assure myself, come from whatever and whoever it is that covers the cosmos.

> The inside
> Of the chamber
> Is invisible;
> What is invisible
> Is immune to
> Penetration:
> Bore holes in
> The void and
> The void remains
> A void;
> And void is
> All that one
> Is left with!

Void! I repeat it to myself! I gaze at the hidden chamber, the impenetrable one, the one that no nail-knife can penetrate through!

> The knife and the sword
> Are nailed to their
> Respective sheaths!

They cry for vengeance
And death against
The door that lies hidden:
They are seething with anger,
Fuming with fury;
The knife's short blade
Turns instantly into
An animal and with
Impatience burrows
Its head into the ground
And strikes the hidden door
With its horns;
The sword wielder smiles
At these antics!

The room remains closed. My vision seems at rest, gathering
its sight, marshalling its armoury of adoration. Adoration and
submission, if they lie prostrate before the Mother, she clears an
opening. That is exactly what happens.

The performing knife
Disappears from the
Hands; the hands are
Empty. Empty to
Adore that which is
Adorable; adorable
Is not relishable
Once the two are
Trained to handle
The knife and the sword,
Penetration hardly
Requires them!

The metamorphoses that swims into his being and into my
becoming transfigures the clearing, the hidden chamber.

The closed chamber
Has no windows even;
A vase with a lid,
A dark house of iron,
They permit no exits,

Allow no entries.
The door of birth,
The window of death
Seal everything.
The void remains
—a Virgin Mother;
and the Void fills
itself only with
its own earth
and for that you
don't need digging
or dredging!

The Presence plays the game. I watch it, relish it, roll it over my tongue. Drops of Mother's vintage wine on the tongue makes it tingle. Not mother-tongue but Mother's tongue! Gently it detaches itself from the mouth and mouthless it spreads across. Spreads across the earth and the sky. An invisible volcano, it galvanises all that is: dog to God, bitch to baboon—everything gets transfigured!

And that transfiguration tolls me back to the ebb and tide of time's river. Questions creep like ants. Puzzles penetrate the skull like bees!

There is honey
That no bee
Is needed to
Produce and
No tongue to
Taste!

The luminous Presence lights up the chamber. I enter and fall....

30

THE POLE AND THE DOOR

He is excited like a boy. (Where is the need for 'like'? He is always a boy!) Reluctant at first, once he accepts something he is agog. He throws himself into that. He seems to lose his identity and become that. Once an idea is lodged in that mind of his, it instantly germinates. Come what may it should reach its result.

I still remember. Somebody telling him. Ghosts haunt that ground. Keep away. Keep away? Nothing can keep him away. (Only Nothing can keep him away. That is another cup of mother's brew!) He waits until dark and with the agility of an angel leaps to the ground. Are there ghosts or ghouls? Drunk with mother's wine the Bhairavas keep guard and he comes back chuckling.

I will make
A ghost of him/her
That says there
Are no ghosts!
I see so many,
I never thought
Ghosts have undone
So many.

I hear, see and stop there. No need to ask him. Illumination comes when need needles you. Until then let it lie: a seed. I gather so many seeds out of greed. Impatient to see them grow, I in fact smother them. They are burnt. But, strangely, I do not, these days, have anything of a regret for things that burn, things that, burning,

burn a hole in the *sahasrara*. Let them burn! They burn through to
the bosom and the heart that lodge the swan.

Excited he is, yes. But not enamoured. Nor excitement as fatal
prelude to addiction. Perhaps, the Great Sculptor that he is, he
makes and breaks moulds with a nonchalance that frees itself from
nostalgia. Make a mould and

Make a form
The mud moulds it;
Break the form,
The mud takes it
Back!
Mud is!
Forms exist,
And all that exists
Gets extinguished.
The Earth-Mother
Is!
Only She is.

The gods and goddesses that pass through his hands into the
mud and mire and then come back gleaming clay models—they
forget that they are gods and goddesses. Let us be mud again. that
way is the chance to pass through his hands. Once again! he mends
the forms that are broken; but make no mistake; he mauls the
forms that think that they cannot be broken. Trust his hands!
Yogakshema lies there. Insurance not for but against life. For
where there is life, there is death and there can be no safety. Safety
lies beyond form and foam, mud and mould. In his/her lap, that is.
"You don't throw away anything even if that is broken. For where
is the space that can contain what you wish to throw away?" he
asks; "thinking that it is broken?" he adds.

"So let me go and get photographed?" he tells me. Photo? Not
a clay model? Not a painting even? Photo? Of all things? I am
amused. Like the stars of the theatres he frequents (once or twice
with me.) he wants a photo. Yes, really amusing.

He is the void
That has no space

And he is the space
That holds the void;
He is the timeless
That gets rolled
Into a clock;
And now he
Wants to get
Through the shutters
Of the camera?
Can the lenses
Write with the
Light of his being,
Transforming
Light into his
Formless form?

Doubts nag me. I see no hope. Perhaps he is playing to the gallery of foolish photographers. "This time," he says, "professionals will take the photo." "Let us see how good they are!" he winks and asks, "Would you like to come?" I am in two minds. This time. Normally I am eager to go. Pester him in a way to take me along wherever he goes. This time: a strange reluctance swallows me whole and soul. Why a photo when I can see him directly? After all, photo of the beloved is an aphrodisiac only when the Beloved is away, far away and long ago. Now that he is near in flesh and blood, why should I be interested in a photo of his?

Make no mistake: a photo of his is not the same as his photo. I make a mistake—always—about this! And learn the devastating difference. "All right! Relax here! The Ganga is so quiet today! Enjoy yourself! After the photo fun and flash I shall be back! Until then happy visions!" He cuts into my reverie on the riverside, gets into the waiting boat and down he goes... down the stream, the endless stream of time. To be framed in a photo and reappear... as and when he can free himself from timelessness.

Devastating difference, I say. I should say the vast differences that nullify the void across time. The difference that marks consciousness as a continuum and physical presence as a terminus. The generic and the universal, that is the difference, the difference between the wave and the sea. In fact, no differences at all. Or, rather, distinction as distinct from difference!

Why I sit on the banks of the river—time and not join him at the photo studio is a mystery to me. Mystery that he leaves unexplained. As unexplained as suddenly your getting a coin of a year that is a century ago. You recognise the year, the figure, the trellice work, the silver—all recognitions of a kind which hardly matters. You can as well do without this kind. But why the coin fell into your hand with all the details in tact but all clues to the details hidden is a mystery. You look at it, marvel at it, hoard it with your usual miserliness but beyond that it is dark, dark, dark.

That is what I feel when I lie there looking into the sky, looking at the trees, looking at the water, at the birds, at the squirrel, at the dogs, at everything. And in fact looking for the only one who, once you look at, you look at everything. That one is gone to a studio! Looking at the lenses even as the lense looks at him. If they look at each other, then only you get the picture. And you can look at them only when both consent to be looked at. Otherwise, what you finally look at may not be what you were prepared to look at.

How many things he makes me look at! Without my knowing that I am looking at them. In fact, I look at him for quite some time, almost every day, without seeing him. Can you believe that? Looking without seeing, seeing without knowing, knowing without realising what you know. The landscape is familiar but the Presence hides behind the man. And, strangest of all, you see him without his allowing himself to be seen, to see; that he is the one who went to get photographed on that day. When the landscape itself feels lonely, lost-forlorn-without him Presence. I sense the Presence and lie in wait. For him to come back.

"You are deranged!" that is what you would exclaim if you know what I mean. And you know what it is to be deranged? Getting out of the ranges of time and space, the ranges of continuity and disruption, the ranges of age, of literally everything that constricts you. Then time is lost, space collapses, persons dissolve and all re-form themselves in a different setting. A difference that seems familiar but familiarity does not crystallise into certainty. The uncertainty goes with twilight language. Substance is felt, symbols are seen differently.

 ` I fall into a long, long slumber. Without dreams, without even sleep, perhaps. That I slumber, I have knowledge. But beyond that, I do not seek to know. That knowing is of no help. What helps is the link, the link that brings you back to the lap. With the toys given again, to choose between the lap and the toy. (Can we not have both? The mother and the toys she creates? Yes, of course, if you merely play with and do not want to stay with the toys!)

"Isn't the photo-session over? I think he is back!" I ask them. They laugh. "Long, long ago it is over. They took several prints. I think one is for you. Perhaps he left it with that one!" I look and see no one. I am neither expecting what is left for me nor do I run to grab it, wrest it from someone who is supposed to give it to me. Let it come when it is to come. You cannot hasten it. You cannot even slow it—once it starts coming. It comes exactly at that moment which is a moment not of time. That I learn.

Does mother come when you want? She comes when you cry. Wanting she does not care for; crying she does. But who will cry for her, he asks. Cry and know nothing but crying, do nothing but crying, wish for nothing except crying. Crying for crying to continue, beyond time, bereft of space. That cry she hears instantly. She can't resist it. She has fatal (congenital) fascination for it. She cares for geneses, not generations. The beginnings which are endings and endings which are more beginnings. But she announces herself in his Presence and all beginnings and endings auspiciously withdraw. The Void fills the Presence; not the Presence the Void.

Down the river I flow with picture cards processed by my lense. (The lense that I keep polishing to perfection but perfection in lense polishing is always a losing game. Of course, the lens he made his favourite singer Ramprasad give me.) Cards that lie in the vaults I carefully preserve. Cautiously, for my own eyes. From the first steps with him. When he locates me among all those who usually surround him. Locates only to lock me up with the key under lock and key with him.

They tell me: "Strange he is, in the studio. The poor fellow doing the job nearly swoons! 'Never seen a face like this!' he says. 'How can a camera take those eyes?' he asks. We all watch. Even as the shot is ready, even before that, we suspect, he is gone to regions where none dare follow, let alone come back from. He, however, comes back. Look at the prints. Pleased, he is. And, strangest of all greets it by putting it at his forehead. Obeisance to one's own picture! Have you heard of a such thing?"

The rest I can imagine. Those eyes I imagine haunt anyone who sees them, anytime. Magic and mystery: I ought to know. I look at them myself and from my looking I can vouch for their enchantment. Those eyes glance at you and you are gone, gone for good, not for the pleasure. For *sreyas*, not *preyas*. Those eyes turn everything upside down.

The forest is the home
The home is the forest;
Friend is foe, foe is friend;
A clod of earth is
The lip of a maiden;
The maiden's lip
Is a clod of earth
Strange the eyes
That see these!

You can even add: the Person, the Presence becomes the Planet (is the Planet!); the Planet is the Person-Presence.

But only I have pictures of those days he spends with me. He is hesitant to tell; but eager that you should come to know. By yourself. Help from me comes, he says, but only when you help yourself. And I do try. Try so far as trying is designed. (to follow a design is to resign yourself to him; perhaps you know it already.) That is how I lie in wait. Lie in ambush, without knowing it. Without the least trace of awareness. Except that the river flows unabated. Unmindful of banks and sands and thresholds.

On the sands of time
The river washes
The pathless land.

I lie on the land
And learn to locate
The path to the
Pathless land.
I make a pretty
Picture, the
Child who is sought
After....
Strangely soothing: those sands. Glistening in the twilight.
Just waiting to be embraced by the night. Light and twilight
crisscross, to my delight. And the delight is infinite: the voice
comes across: "Did you see those photos of mine?" he asks.

31

THE LOVER IS THE MOTHER, TOO

In an instant he materialises himself. Do not get the word wrongly. The Presence is physical. Assumes a name and a form. That is what the word means. Do not have illusions developing round it. It is rational, as rational as notional name and form permit. *Nama* and *rupa*, he says, is a block of ice that forms out of the shoreless ocean of liquid water. Give it a name, it is only a form. Give it a form, it is only a name. If you are attached to them they work. Even if you do not need them he doesn't stop working.

"What happens after your photo session?" I feel like asking. But decide it is meaningless. What happens to a block of ice when it loses its 'icy' form? It gets its original formlessness, from which all forms rise. So no need for questions about intervening time. Specially for the One who passes through time to pass into eternity.

• "I like these quiet sessions with you," he begins. "I am inclined to say that." He adds taking away the germ of smugness just surfacing. "Quite often I feel like saying you are not what I am not. But I know it is hard for you to believe it." "You know...," he is about to say. This time I do know: "believable lies and unbelievable truths," that is what he says. This ingenuous way with words which are not just words, he always has.

I still recall my interest in *Brahma Sutras*. Tough text; not for delicate palates. I enjoy its mystifying but resilient dialectic. Of course, I do not always understand what I enjoy. 'Enjoy without understanding' could as well be an exhortation. And reveling in its resilience I find myself stumped one morning. He is in an irrepressible mood of fun. "Spiritual ragging," he calls it. And suddenly he announces, "Do not stop with *Brahma Sutras*." "Yes, I should read other texts, the Gita...." He looks amused. Certainly in a mood to laugh everything off—mood of putting a sharp knife through the fat butter of pontification, of pretension. "One has alongside *Brahma Sutras*, *Bhrama Sutras*, too!" he says with an unmistakable glint in the eye.

Brahma Sutras point to the reality that is. Bhrama Sutras pinpoint the illusions that surrounds the reality that is. But if reality is, then illusion cannot be. How can they both coexist? Or, are they coterminous with each other? Why the need for this and that? "Can you have a positive without a negative?" he asks. "Can you get a photograph without a negative?" I understand. Yes, that is true. For a photo you should have a photo film. It must have a chemical coating. Then only it can photograph and give you a print. (Is this true? I wait to know.)

"Just think. There may be pictures which are photos. And photos which are pictures," he continues. This time I am foxed. I scarcely follow the logic. (as if logic is the last resort! Of course, it is the last resort of the one who is lost!) I do not even try to wriggle myself out of the riddle. Conundrums. *Viruddha Satya:* logical fallacies. Irreconcilables. I get into knots. Let me leave it to him. (You do not think "You let him!" the truth is "he lets you.")

I fall into the network of *bhrama*. So soothing. Illusions do not need logic. They simply allow you to float in them. To catch you unawares, to trap you. And then to release you. Re-lease the logic you seem to have lost. Aphorism of reality and axioms of illusion: between them they play the game. You just be. They play with you and, again in a moment of sheer awareness both flash on the plate of the mind.

His coming back after that photo finish is itself a marvel to me. I do wait but I hardly suspect the second coming. That I read as a poem. Enjoy it as a metaphor. Explicate it nicely. But actual second coming? Thank you! Don't take me for a ride. That just is not possible. Perhaps, probable but not possible. Time and space

don't permit it. You must be too much of a dumb one to even think
of it.

The second coming I mean. And in the meantime he manages
to reach me a print that he went to be made of him. It is radiant,
absolutely radiant. Until I see it I never know how original it can
appear, a photo. I keep it where I can always see it. The heart is the
best place. It is there that all prints are made. And if your heart has
the right equipment, unbelievable lies become demonstrable
truths. Here the secret is the eye of the heart. The heart lends its
glasses to the eye. And the eye sees things which, without the
heart, it cannot see at all.

Seeing him and viewing the photo: points that give rise to
persistent doubts. Where is the resemblance? Even semblance?
That photo that day seems to have done something to him. He is
more withdrawn. Polite, even affectionate but 'this far and no
further!' he seems to say. A ring of felt but inexplicable change.
Certainly there is a sea-change (or river change? The Godavari
instead of the Ganga?) And I feel the ground slippery. Like the
hole that is filled with earth even as he goes on digging!

I have a hole in the head. An aperture seems to open itself.
The *sahasrara* seems to yield itself to that hole which even as I see
becomes a tunnel, a tunnel of time. Strange things appear in and
through the tunnel. I see him before the beginning of the tunnel: it
becomes a maze, a labyrinth now. He is at the end of the tunnel but
is in a maze now.

I shall go crazy! Possible revelations in and through the tunnel
unnerve me. "Horrific links," he says. Now I can recognise him.
Not the form, but the voice. That is unnerving. That is, certainly,
intriguing. The same gestures, the same gaiety and joy, the same
fondness for songs, specially Ramprasad's. But I can not see him.
Or, I see him but don not seem to see through. He, perhaps, does
not want it yet!

I hug to my bosom the One I am used to. Being used to has
great advantages. He talks to you freely, holds you easily, cajoles
you, caters to nearly every whim that you can trump up. And he
fulfils it. Like indulging a spoilt brat.

"Why you should have gone for that photo without me, beats me!" I say. Finally, the resentment long boiling inside explodes. "Oh! You still bother!" he says and laughs it off. I am peeved. No laughing it off. I want ιo get to the mystery of it. That particular gesture of putting his head to his own photo, still bothers me. Does he want me to note it specially? Is there something special about it?

"There is," he says. "That is something special." And, he adds, "Learn to be patient. Did I not tell you that before?" Yes, he did. So many times. But I learn slow, if at all. "You are too impatient, you know that?" he asks. Yes I am. I felt like telling him. You made me that way. Why blame me? I have nothing to do with what I am. Given the chance to be what I am and do what I like I would have wrested your secret from you long, long ago! I would not have hemmed and hawed and waited in the wings.

"You say patience! And yet you say longing is necessary. Is it not the end of patience the beginning of longing?" I tell him. I sound smug: "Impatient I am, but see how clever I am" that is what I want to tell him. "I am not a *bewakoof*...," I announce. He bursts out laughing. At the word or at me. I hardly know. But laughing with love for the child who suddenly sounds precocious. Precocity always amuses a father, I suppose. "I am a fool but not naive!" "Oh! Is it!" "Yes, it is," I tell him and subside. "Everything has to have its proper moment," he says. And I can guess the rest. "It's predetermined, well-meant moment," he would say.

We enjoy the drama meanwhile. The actors are bustling about on the stage. Some come and talk to him with make-up even. Interval between scene and scene. How he enjoys the illusions of the stage always beats me hollow. He is, in fact, in his element there. I always feel you should catch him in his own scenes on his own stage. I seem to get over my sulking. I join the fun. I really enjoy it. Nostalgia. For the lover and the lass hugging each other on the stage. How lucky! Looking at me, he gives a knowing wink. I pretend innocence. Perhaps I am also getting to be good at acting!

Let him talk to the actors and actresses. What have I to do with it or with them? They bore me. Actors I can not stand. Their acting,

I stand and understand! "You seem to be restive," he says. So I did
not enjoy the thing at all! No hiding it from him. "He is slightly
older! So let him go and take rest," he announces to those around
him. And they promptly bundle me out.

I don not mind. Not in the least. In fact, I gloat over the fact
that I got over the need for his presence. (Not his Presence, mind
you.) The banks of the river are for me. Its waves are so many
hands caressing you. His hands. The mother's hands. Even her
fear-inducing, fatal hands fascinate me (though fascination often is
the other side of real fright.) I like to be alone. Give me the river,
the sky, the birds—the distant noise of people bustling about...
enough for me.

> Lying on the banks
> Of the river
> I look at my
> Mother and Father
> In such radiance
> That the river
> Is a shy bride
> Who looks away
> From them.
> Even as they
> Enter her!

Images amaze me. So many camera shots that I am the
amazing camera. Camera that snaps, shoots and develops
instantly. The Paramahamsa Brand Polaroids. Among many, one
shot detaches itself and develops. On its own, on her own. Just see.

That young woman with matted locks in orange robes. What
is she doing here, in this garden of delights? How dare she disturb
the peace. The Paramahamsa has no need for anyone except the
mother. Then how come! And strangely he is there, too. Gesturing
to me: "Relax! Mother wants her to be here! If you can watch!
Perhaps this needs all your watching." I get the message. I stop
being startled (a habit that needs correction: getting amazed and
startled often, quite often.). I suspend everything and append
everything in, of and about me into my eyes. (Why do you not say
'I am eyes all over'? Yes, that is it.)

Then the eyes see the other. The young mother has become the other. Is it? No. I distinctly see both. The one with the matted locks is directing the other one with neatly combed hair. Exceptionally elegant, that one. Beautiful in an intoxicating way. Mother perhaps took special care in moulding this lump of clay. ('Lump of clay?' he once admonished me, adding 'lamp of consciousness.') Attractive in a fascinating way. What I see. She is quite plump (all lovely lumps of clay are plump! I once punned and he scolded me for unwarranted *slesha*, pun.) I now see what I did not notice earlier. She has the face I seem to have seen somewhere. Strong memories of having seen her face teases me. Several snaps rush through the camera that I am. No identifying tag below any one snap. All are anonymous.

This one is particularly familiar. Doubtless familiar. Must have seen her somewhere with him. Elsewhere, not here. Not here.

Her eyes are
Ecstatic with
Her smile,
Playing hide and seek.
In the dark
Bushes her
Smile is the
Bouquet of flowers.
The radiance
On the face is like
The foam that frolics
On the bosom of the ocean
As waves
On her swelling breasts
The radiant smile
Is like a white bodice.
Adoration to you
Bhavatarini!

That clinches the vision. Yes, I see her, I saw her earlier, everywhere, the Mother with her lolling tongue and dripping blood is now the woman, the coy mother, the potential *sakti*.

The one with the matted locks. She is beckoning to him: "Lie
in her lap and let the rhythm of her breath lull you as on the waves
of the ocean of consciousness," she seems to be saying. "Just lie
there and the universe itself cajoles you. The wind god is
breathless to see and stops in his stride; the dark that fills the night
is shielding you from prying eyes. The river is not allowing any
boat to cross. Her *jagat* is without *jagrat*! That is her play!"

The last word spoken, the vision takes over. Perhaps, the
lenses are changed. The master's magnifying lenses: "*lumagni*" it
is. Luminous *agni* that burns to ash the taint in the eye, the mote in
the mind. I can not bear the vision. What have I done to qualify for
what I see now:

The usually tall
Presence is now
No longer tall.
Oh! My! The
Magic of the mother
Is her lila:
The tall one is a
Small one now.
A child in body
As always he is in mind!
How he jumps into
Her lap!
The lap of the Mother
Long sought after
Willingly, gloriously
Surrenders now to
Rock the child
In her lap.

How deceitful our eyes are. Such a soul-enthralling re-union.
And we do not have use for the eyes she gives, herself. And you
borrow extra eyes and burrow your head in the scorching sand that
gorges your eyes. And the mother is a woman lusted after. The
mother is a skeleton dug to place on the tables for dissecting the
body. Not in sacrifice but in sheer vice.

The enormity of the vision, the Presence, engulfs me even as my guilt gullitones me. I have to bear the cross. Not of Christ (How light that would be to carry since it is made of light.) but of my own making. The cross I make to nail myself. With him there, looking after you, helpless 'I want to come to you. But the skeletons in your cupboard block me.' I shiver.

I shiver and a cold coming of that shiver makes the spine slumber. I begin to curse myself and come near to blaming everything. Moments of desperation madden me. Has the vision vanished? Is it a chimera? Some trip induced by *bhang*?

The lover is
The mother too;
The other is
The Beloved, too;
Balance the bifocals
You get a clear vision!

I still lie on the sands staring into space. For forms that emerge and merge in the space of my being.

32

THE 'I' BEHIND ALL EYES

He calls me, on his own. I bide my time for the call. Living with my usual depression-elevation rhythm, I re-view my situation. Conflicting views confuse me. What he is no one seems to say with any amount of conviction. Either they go into ecstasy or they pester him with their problems. I feel increasing alienation from them. Perhaps, they do not pander to my ego. That could be the reason for feeling a sense of detachment. Or, it could also be emotional frustration. Above all, a desperate need for clarity about things dogs me. If I get the words, I do not follow the voice. When the voice is familiar, an unfamiliar vision baffles me.

The voice is familiar
The words are not;
The dialect
Of the ancient night
Gores my throat
The day does not heal;
Roaming across ages
I try to decipher the alphabet;
A thick film flays recognition.
A few letters escape
But the night stands guard
Over word-formation
The dialect is inviolate.

Inviolate, immaculate. One could go on and on. His words burn holes in the heart. I hardly attempt anything. Feel I should simply annihilate myself. Disappear without a trace. Go for long, long sleep-unending, unquestioning unawareness. Just be. The Presence is. But nothing that seems to matter is what that Presence is.

Imagination condensed becomes the reality, they say. But when reality that needs no imagination to condense himself stares you in the face, where is the need for imagination. Reality is what I precisely experience (even if it is perfunctory). But this reality is precisely what I do not know many things about. Can you not see the desperation?

I can see the Presence clearly. For that no special eye is needed. But then seeing is of no use. Seeing does not seem to bore holes for pegs of understanding to be hung. The Mother who is allusive and the Other who is clearly seen-in effect, both baffle you. The one you have to construct through *bhavana*; the other is just before you. Palpable, tangible. Laughs, talks, cracks your fingers, eats with you. Yet, illumination is impervious to perception.

Hints and guesses; guesses more than hints. Voice more than words; letters more than speech. Distance more than nearness. All conspire; conspire to catch you in conundrums. Is the needle of the mind still retaining some flue so that the delicate thread does not pass through the eye? Are perceptions so opaque that nothing could be seen. Is it my fault? Is my fault something that I create? Or is it something con-genital? In that case my fault and I get divorced.

The glow of experience already tasted becomes dim. Awareness is not linear. Addictions make the awareness sharp. That is the amazing thing. Only my addictions give me my insights. (Big word! Do you have any? I hear someone whispering.) That I have addictions which impede clear insight is itself an insight free from addiction. To the extent I know there is an addiction in me, to that extent the needle's eye is clear. But then it is my addiction that ensures constant creative awareness.

"I did not see you. For quite a long time. So I write a letter," he says. Yes, I did get it. I did not know that he wrote/writes letters.

That, sure, is a revelation. "All familiar things are revelations to
you!" he laughs. Yes, that is true. Things do surprise me. What is
the big deal if you receive a letter?

That is what I think. Then he says: "You know what your
letters to me are? A *bhakta* writes a letter and it is a *Purana* to me.
I can even smell the contents. Those from worldly fellows stink. I
can not bear them. I throw them away. Throw them away as if they
are snakes ready to sting you. But let a seeker write-seekers of
peace, I mean—it awakens mothers' awareness in me!" (as if he
requires a stimulus!)

Amazing! Even astounding. Could letters have that impact?
Then, I remember, once they reach the Mother, letters—*aksharas*-
become revelations, *darshana*. They are *matrikas*. He infuses
illumination into them. Then they are carriers of awareness,
continuing semi-conductors of consciousness. It is not what I
write but how s/he reads it that is important.

Perhaps I tend to forget that anything—literally anything—
can (and does) get him into that leap that makes him soar into
chidakasha. Until you see the *chamatkar* you couldn't believe
such a thing exists. That anything is enough for him to take off.
You close an umbrella; and that noise is enough to open his
chinmaya sakti, the power of consciousness. So tuned, so
sensitive: every little bit of experience a trigger for explosion into
the endless spaces of cosmic consciousness. And that space is
space where you also are, he says. "You can not be anywhere
else!" he affirms.

"Everything is hung in infinite space which I am and all that is
hangs like diamonds in a necklace," he says. I listen to the music
of his affirmation. To the miracle of his voice which is the
Presence. "Everything exists and exists in everything," he says. I
hear casually, hear it as pleasing poetry. As poetic legitimation of
an indefensible exaggeration. Charming in its own way but
beyond that charm; no, I am not going to stretch it further. The
contours of a poem: that is where the affirmation belongs. I can
even write like that to impress (the clientele of poetry):

The magnifying glass

Lying in the lap of love
Rocks itself to
Luminous sleep
Lulling the images to
Uncoil themselves.
The eyes bulge
In their sockets.

"That is nice. But you do mean that those words mean what they are meant to mean? Do you?" he laughs uproariously and asks. I hesitate. Now that he asks, I do not mean exactly what they mean. "They mean exactly what they mean. Make no mistake about it," the voice is gentle but firm.

I ruminate on those words. I can not say I meditate. When I feel like meditating the eyes are filled with tears. Burning tears that thirst for the One to crystallise himself through those tears. Perhaps, tears are themselves the form of his Presence. But how do we shed tears for him if we have not shed them for something or the other, for someone or the other? How do we ensure that there are tears at all? Most eyes are dry. Dry as dust to death. Heroic men, they are stoic. They think tears are womanly, effeminate effusions of nervous weakness!

"I do not know how to put it across to you...," he says. Through tears, I suppose, that is the response I wish to offer. But keep the counsel to myself. "The tears I shed for Mother, for you all, would fill seven seas and leave enough to fill another unendingly"—a heart-rending sigh escapes him. He is visibly ill. I do not see any reason for his illness. No manifest reason, except the only reason that there are many things reason cannot reason out. The face is racked with visible pain; a sorrow I hardly notice. So far I do not even suspect that.

So jovial he is; so full of zest for life. Brimming with joy. Radiant with love. That is the face I see. I always wish to see. But what I wish to see could as well be what he does not wish to show. "Just as you are full of tears for him, he may also be full of tears for you, for all of us!" someone says. Possible. His longing for her children. Children who have gone astray; kids who are prodigal and tug at and tear her breasts. Kids who kill each other, who ransack the earth, rape the sources and resources. Wayward, wanton, vicious—beyond redemption.

"There is none beyond Mother's redemption, you can take it from me," he cuts in firmly. I yield. Yes, he knows. He knows the total picture. I see only a part of it and jump to my foolhardy conclusions. He is silent and sad. "I am sad because you do not see what I see and pester me to show you what I see." That is true. How does he see? Like us? With our 'own' eyes? Or eyes which are actually his on loan to us and then brashly, shamelessly claimed as our own? I tell him:

"I like your
Eyes most.
I wish I had
Them for myself,
For ever!"
"I don't mind
grafting them on
to you. Painlessly, too.
But then
You should look/see
With those eyes alone.
If you think
You could do that
Take them:
Here they are!"

The lines cajole, console, soothe my being. I fall into slumber again. I dream: everywhere I see and I see only those eyes. Nothing else. Not a single pair of any other. Wherever vision takes me there his eyes bulge through the holes. "There are no other eyes, except mine; all eyes are mine. I see through them all," he whispers. Whisper because you can not bear the loudly proclaimed truth. The truth has to come gently. Or, through a narrative. Or, even a picture. For, what is a narrative except a moving picture? And what is a picture card except a frozen narrative?

The *aswatha* tree
Has leaves all over
Its branches

And all the leaves
Are so many
Camera snaps
That show
His radiant face!
Behind the leaves, he is: the leaves do not cease to be leaves
because he appears on them. Shuffle them: the face hides the rear;
shuffle them again, the rear hides the face.

"I think you are right. But you still have uneasy moments of
doubt. Doubt which gently worms its way into the fruit of faith."
Like Takshaka worming his serpent body into Parikshit's fruit.
Like Parikshit I too, would like to examine the proof....

33

THE CAMERA THAT HOLDS THE VISUAL
AND THE VISIONARY

"I have brought this toy for you!" he announces cheerfully. And puts the gadget (the spelling is wrong; it should be 'God's jest!') in my hands. Toy? It is an expensive camera. "I got it from that studio man who took my photo long ago. He says he can spare it. Of course, I saw to it that it is functioning even after what looks like such a long, long time. More than a century!" he says.

He is, again, exuberantly, radiantly cheerful. The smile is back on the face. (Does it leave the face at any time? That it appears to leave is part of his *maya* and *manas*!) the sorrow that sorrow is, is cleverly (carefully?) hidden. Even Mother does not know what he has up his sleeve. (And he wears full sleeves!) Looking at the gleaming thing, I feel fascinated. And slightly embarrassed. I never handle the thing. If I can help it, that is. And I can not help it this time. "You regret that you were not there with me at that studio. Now you yourself take the photographs. I shall pose for you. Wherever you want me to. But I want them to be taken by you, by yourself." He emphasises, 'yourself'. Emphases, his emphases, alas, are often not heard; though heard, rarely heeded. That is how this thing happens. This fun of the photo-taking session. (As funny as the one that Arjuna was shown in that other play—hour of the Playful God!)

What does he lack? He loads the thing with his own 'cosmic' reel. Opens the shutter, looks at the lenses, adjusts the focus (looks straight into my eyes) and says, "Snap! And snap it up!" With

imperceptible ecstasy suffusing the face. With joy spread all over.
And we take the snaps all over the piace. We roam all over literally
looking for vantage points. And so many angles! I never could
imagine that the piace could hold so many angles! That he could
pose for and from so many facets. My eyes bulge looking through
the lenses. Seeing him through the lenses is... how shall I put it?

Let me try. The trying is desperate. One can look at pictures
easily. But if the picture is not what you see through the lense and
what you see through the lense—with your eyes—is himself then
what do you see? Is that what I see?

I see through
The lense clearly:
It is he himself.
I see at the
Snap; and what
The lense shows me
And what I see
Through the lense
(or, imagine I see!)
are not the same!

When do you prefer poetry? When you try to freeze the macro
experience into a micro frame; when you try to put into a *sloka*
form what the best *sloka* cannot contain. The diminution in space
and time baffles you. And the photos that emerge are his certainly.
But not his in the sense in which you use the pronoun!

What I see and
What he shows
Are poles apart!
I flatter myself
That my eyes
Can see clearly
And the eyes
Themselves revolt
And revoke this
Naivete!
You can never see

That which he
Permits you to see
Until you
Change your views
Of what he permits
And what he does not!
Sounds incoherent? Incoherence is a mild experience.
Compare it to what I see.

Over aeons of time
Frames criss-cross,
Transfigure and
What is seen is
Not what is viewed,
And sight itself,
In the process,
Becomes suspect.

He speaks casually about the First Cause: "I am extinct! And I merge into the five elements!" Strange affirmation from a stranger Presence. The camera dare not disobey him; or, rather, she loves him too daringly to disobey him. Thus I see with eyes that he grafts.

Hidden in the
Foliage he comes!
The dense forest
Curls itself
Into abandon
The birds sing
With the same beak:
"what is this
crazy thing?
I see things
I never saw
Through the lense!"
And even as I gaze and gaze and gaze
The thick foliage
Hides forms

That seem
To reveal
Themselves,
Even as the
Foliage transfigures
Itself;
In disbelief
I wipe 'my'
Eyes; yes,
The leaves lie
Low to reveal
Forms that they
Conceal from
The prying eye.
So many figures
On the green
Foliage that
Figuring them
Out is to count
The stars in the sky!
And
In a corner
The Beloved bares
Himself.
Sudden the baring,
Sharp the focus,
And he enters
The eyes and
Fills the void,
No longer a void
But vibrant space,
Animate, moving
With the sky above
And the earth below
In the strides of Vamana.
Thus in the universe that she vomits forth

The leaves are
And aren't!
The foliage is
And isn't!
The transfiguration
Is and isn't!
A squirrel peeps
At you and winks:
"the Lord is here!"
Then I see
The earth's lush,
Green carpet
Is green with envy:
"My Lord, I insist,
should walk on
my carpet and
on nothing else!
Let others dare,
They cannot be as
Green as I am!
This is the original
Green the Lord
Himself lovingly
Frames and before
Framing, forms!
I yield in delight
When his touch
Makes me bashful!"

The green carpet communicates in communion; the new cable
on the ground recently laid communicate nothing. The earth
watches the play:

The voices wilt into a wail;
The sounds stretch across
The withered fields.
The cables are baffled;
Allergic to strange codes, they

Cannot comfort the cobs awaiting
Rain
The cables whisper:
"we need new programming.
We need new vocabulary;
Only the flower garden
Winking at her can
Catch the code!"
Perhaps, the cables do get across:
Light filters itself
Through the thick leaves:
Hesitant at first
To touch the bare branches
And the barer trunks,
It gathers courage
For light knows:
"I alone can write
forever; things
written in light
remain in light."
The chirping birds
Nod their beaks
In assent: they
Summon up sounds
From space and
break into a melody
that the cables do
not reach out!
They are not needed
The birds are adequate!
Oh, my! The earth mother is playing strange tricks
Beside a hole
That is a well undefiled,
Mother licks
Mud into shape
So tenderly, with

Such grace and
Finesse that the
Mud, a coy mistress,
Yields herself in
Delight into his hands.
See! The *ghat*
Brimming with water,
Beside the hole,
With the leaves overseeing,
Exult in the act
Of creation that brings
Them into being.
But wait,
"My" eyes
wipe themselves
with the hanky
of faith:
(He really creates
one for me!)
the *mrinmaya*
becomes *chinmaya*
snow-white chicks
—the original colour
not the alchemical!-
stroll near the
ghata, the *mrinmaya*
in sheer joy of
strolling near their
mother hidden in the
leaves! (Is she
hatching more chicks?
The *anda* for the
Brahmanda?)
Must be; the
Karmic pots flaunt
The gods in a riot!

How madly they
Create!
Creation that camouflages
Every secret
Even as the hole
Covers itself with the
Earth!
The earth mother
Needs secrecy:
In the strict privacy
Of the womb she
Shapes—with no noise,
With no chisel
With no strokes!
Only the chicks know!
But they have no
Word-cables to convey.

I remain immersed in the experience: the experience that is visionary as well as visual. The visual becomes the visionary. Since my eye is not ripe enough for direct, unmediated experience of the cosmos, photos do the job of "inducing" the implications. I marvel at the range, at the rapturous range that the limitless *prakriti* presents before the eye.

I look again
At the visuals:
They unravel
Mystery after mystery
The mystery that
Is nature and nature
That is the mystery.
Am I in Krishna's
Lila-kshetra?
The cows have a
Familiar look:
I have seen them
Earlier, elsewhere.

That I can vouch.
Yes, that is true:
The twilight hour
—the hour that marks
the return of the
cattle home with the
dust from the earth mother's
bosom emitting a fragrance
that is not of the earth!
The flute-player is hidden.
But, then
The Mother has space
For the buffaloes too;
Ah! Yes, the slayer
Of the Buffalo Demon,
Mahishasura Mardini-
dances in the eyes:
"see lad! The horns
protrude: that is
natural for the animal:
but when they intrude
as pride in the human
and threaten the
rhythm I set for
nature then I
do cut the horns off
—mercilessly.
With the horn of pride
Removed, the blinkers
That veil the eye
Disappear
And Pasupati,
Now the Lord of the Animals,
Sees me in my full glory!"
She tells.

But, I realise, some are exceptional. Born with no pride, they dance in ecstasy on the mother's lap. Bereft of the buffalo, they in fact create one. All is, they realise from birth, clothed in and for them. They are the *nitya-lila sishu*: the eternal play-boy. Their childhood will never be over. In fact, it never begins, therefore there is no question of its ending. The vision of the boy entrances me. But he is not alone. He brings down his companions to assist the play, to play his assistants.

He is the tallest
Of the four:
The other three
Resist re-cognition
Of varied frames,
Varied heights,
They are, together,
The symphony and
The harmony that
Marks his Presence.
See one is even
Placing his hands
On his shoulder
—what luck of
familiarity is this?
In moments of madness
I visualise the one
Who rode on his back!
The fields that surround
Them wink in complicity:
"Yes, he has his hands
on your shoulders firmly:
lest you are tempted
to defect, he himself
clasps you!"

I laugh in visionary delight. Delight that leaves me breathless: the inner being flexes her wings. "More is to be seen! Serve and conserve-that way only revelations come!"-she cautions me. I do need this caution. For, late in time, old in age, I arrive on the scene. Energy for exertion is not equal to enthusiasm for exertion. I have to, I know, hold in balance both energy and enthusiasm on one side and his grace and love on the other. "More than anything else," he declares, "I require love. My hunger for it is ravenous!" For love, age is nothing. In every age and at any point of age and time this love is available. For the sake of this love the aged become young; the young even forfeit the shell of youth. The collapse of identities is the culmination. The boy has no need for it: He has no idea that such collapse is needed. The aged too do not need it for they are back in their childhood.

> Resting and relaxed
> The ancient one
> Sits with the meru, the pillar,
> Behind his back!
> His animal grazes
> In the background;
> He is the bearded one
> This time:
> Grinning slyly
> With the fire
> In his hand.
> Father can do nothing
> Than rest, after
> Dissolution, until
> The call for creation
> Rises in the heavens
> Once again: until
> Then he rests. Holding
> The *layagni*, the
> luminous fire of dissolution
> in his hand!

Like the faithful *sunaka* that accompanies Dharmaraja I wait near him with his hands caressing me. He is obviously delighted- the child that he is, he detaches himself impulsively from his 'cronies' and taking the dog away from them roams all around. Is Ramalal near? I haven't seen him, yet. I wait fascinated for the eye

that reveals to roam as it fancies—anything to register, for that
which is registered to reveal her splendour.

The thatched huts
In the field
Outside the village
Glimmer in the
Gathering twilight.
His nativity floods
The eye with unshed
Tears:
This is the hut
He chooses to
Enter-always.
The cities have
Cracks in their walls;
The hut is a mansion
For this beetle-bee.
But see
How the mother bends
With age-weight,
Weary with wayward
Kids who leave things
Broken, things to be
Mended, things to be
Moulded again.
She pins her hopes,
As always, on the
Kid in the thatched hut!
And he never betrays the Mother.

"But," he whispers, "the mother seems to be bent with age,
with time. She cannot in reality be. She is the Mahakala, the
Conqueror, the Vanquisher of Time itself. Get all other snaps out!
And see this One, she is the Many!" Everything dissolves itself.
There is a collapse of images; the collage is over. All in one, one in
all: it is now the One who is beckoning to me. Supreme moments
that see the One and yet do not bypass the many; the many
perceive the One that remains. Both heavens, shadows and shapes

remain in and of the One. A flood of beauty engulfs the earth. The
Mother breaks through the walls of the temple. Her blazing fury is
now her benign smile. Her four arms are no longer fierce or
fantastic: they embrace in their folds everything, literally
everything. The Cosmic Form transfixes:

Mother!
Thou art the
Object of Perception
And you distribute
The earth-forms;
The Producer of
Cosmos, you support
All that is the
Cosmos
You are the nourishing grain,
The quenching water,
The igniting fire,
The supporting earth
All forms merge in
You, as, I, one of
Thy infinite moulds
Lapse into your lap.

34

THE DESCENT

"You are too demanding, too exacting for my taste," I tell him. Point blank, I think. "Even after showing you everything and telling all... you still think like that?" he asks. I am wary. I hardly know he would be so quick to retort. If you could call it a retort. (He is incapable of cutting any one down to size with a retort; for all sizes are shaped by him). I still feel that I should tell him a few things. Things that others tell me about him. (Or rather things that he makes others tell me.) "Why can you not tell all these things yourself? Why should I get them from others when I see and talk to you nearly every day?" I whine peevishly.

"You will be happy, will you, if I go about dancing and getting on to the roof of everyone's house and declare 'I am Rama! I am Krishna!'" he taunts. No, he knows I would not be happy that way: with that kind of affirmation. I like mystery, I like the miracle of revelation to come like leaves to a tree, so naturally, so gently and, above all, so unobtrusively. I like him to be that way: aloof but attached; revealing yet concealing; loving yet freezing you from the fetters that pass for love. And not a word about himself: Not even by a slip of the tongue. If his/her tongue slips, time you got ready for apocalypse of every tongue on earth! As Ramprasad would say, 'Did he at any time categorically affirm anything about himself?' Yes, that is just like the Mother. You can affirm something only when you deny that something to other things. Or, rather affirmation and denial are cancelling categories. So you say neither this nor that. "Think in whatever way it suits you. That is

right and what is right with you is all right with me. I
accommodate myself—I have no problem. All problem is yours!"

I remain silent. "I even remove my glasses for you! Don't you
see?" he asks again. So articulate in the beginning I remain
speechless now. Except for speech that says nothing in and
through words:

Why do you
Shield your eyes
With glasses
Almost always?
"Glasses? Me?
That's a laugh.
I think you
Require to
Remove—yours!"
He says.

"Yes. I want to remove my glasses and speak...," I say again.
"Whether you have your glasses on or off, the thing does not
change. Your sight has no relevance for that!" he tells point blank
this time.

The sheer joy of being in his place is like a shot in the arm to
me. So full of "zest, zing and zap" (pardon *tantra* words) that I
come very near to climbing the trees, climbing even the railings in
a building.... It is inexplicable (and that is the way it should be, he
says.) The tank across the home is the condensed water of all the
seven seas that circle the globe. The tall trees are straight from
heaven: the *Parijatas*, they are. The orchards are no less than
Nandana-vana, the grooves of the blue-eyed boy. The twilight
hour in that place drives me mad!

Seeing the husking machine
In the thatched hut
He is born into
Hushes me into silence;
Stone well and devotion
Go together! He crushes
The grain into flour!
None can escape.

"Stop your effusions and tell me what you were told by the others. Specially by the one whom I dragged to come with me and who I saw to it was born a few hours after I...," he pauses and I fill up the blanks "after you were 'cosmically introduced?' right?" He laughs at my memory: yes, this chap remembers my exact words!

I cease speaking. I cease even seeing. I cease the distance between us and hurl it aside. I must do all this. It is necessary. Only then I can tell him without tiring him, tell about what he already knows.

"There is nothing that you can tell me that I need to be told," he gently re-minds. "But tell me because you love to tell me. And if confirmation of what you tell is what your telling implies, forget it. Cool your breath to save your..." "*sambar*" I laugh adding the word. He, too, laughs but adds a bite: "I do not need to be told. I need to be loved!" And after a pause, looking for fish in the lake, says, "They all tell me they love me. And beyond telling that, there is hardly anything to show that they love me...." They love themselves more than they love him....

I begin to doubt. Whether I love him, myself. For that, I know, I have to discard all other forms that come very near to telling you that they are love. Love has no displaced subterfuges. That it seems to have them is his play from which he wants you to recover, that is, re-cover him, and re-covering is love.

That, it outwardly strikes me, is why he is born with no covering, with even no eyes to see his entry into and from the Mother. I meditate on the mystery of re-covery. Of recovering the moment. "Meditate so that total merging makes viewing natural...."

I do, in sheer joy. Effortlessly words that I hear assume forms....

The small house, in fact, a thatched hut, is shrouded in darkness, the village is asleep. Even during the day, the village shows no bustling activity. It seems always to be sedate. (Perhaps, to date, too, it is still sedate.) Only there is more than normal animation in this house tonight. A scene of expectant hush invades the house. A child is expected to be born. The mother is in labour (and when the child is born, the mother acquires her culmination as a woman) and any minute the wonderful child would change from one mother's 'micro-womb' to the Mother's 'macro-womb'—if you would permit the use of 'micro' and 'macro'.

Who would believe then that the child delivering himself to the cosmos would go through the *maya* of growing up and becoming a byword for love as incarnate divinity? Would the father and mother themselves be aware that the birth is a momentous event? All are conundrums. But the fact is intriguing....

Strange things happen. Rather, not strange at all. We do have precedents. When the blue-eyed boy took cosmic birth in the prison and had to be whisked away to his foster-mother-even as the few-hours-kid-by his father, everyone around underwent strange sensations. Mainly the sensation of drowsiness and sleep. All of them except Vasudeva were lulled gently into sleep. This is, for many, a story charmingly poetic, touchingly melodramatic. Enjoyable as art is enjoyable—the joy of illusion, of make-believe.

But that exactly is what happens now. The child does come out of the womb but the womb is *ayonija*, immaculate! Radiant, luminous and lovely, the child makes his dramatic entry into creation more dramatic. Peer into the small enclosure where he takes birth: except the mother who seems asleep, there is no one in the "room". Literally no one. Not even a *mantra sani*! What do you call her? A midwife. She, too, is nowhere near the child, indeed nowhere to be seen in the room. What a name! *Mantra sani* 'midwife' as translation is a misnomer. All are sunk in drowsiness and naturally the One born in prison, himself, made the statement: what is night for others is day for the *yogi*!

The enclosure he has chosen to introduce himself into is empty. Except the Mother who is asleep, no, one else, literally no one else, is present. An unearthly (therefore heavenly) quiet rules the hours. No one dare stir even in sleep. The night is so wholesome that no discordant note, no negative motif is struck anywhere. Only the child laughs even as he prevents anyone from 'seeing' his descent. Perhaps the immaculate entry is a sight for the gods and no human eye can desecrate its immutable sanctity by peering at it....

I know and I realise that I can hardly put it across to you. The descent is like the fall of a gentle dewdrop on the lotus leaf. When it comes, when it drops not even the lotus can perceive and tell. The only alternative is to allow the love—eye to take over... and once that eye operates doors open where you least expect them. Avenues open up in unexpected moments:

The serene-looking
Child nestles on
The bed, beside the mother
In a mist of melodious
Slumber that the cosmos
Itself is rooted into!
A silence that is itself,
And is nothing else,
Reigns supreme.
The five elements
Mark the entry by
Their own *mouna*
The Lordly Child
Beckons to them:
"I shall embody
myself in you,
even as you give
form and frame to
my Formless, Timeless,
Spaceless Being!"

I remain drowsy: only through a haze I can see all that is taking place. Haze? Perhaps I am not right. It is through the film of love and the lense of eternity I see. I can hardly see the mystery, even then. Even when he permits you to visualise it, the vision itself withdraws in haste. In fear and haste. "This is something beyond me..." the visionary eye cries, in utter helplessness.

The descent of the
Incarnate being
Is not for the eye to see;
What the eye sees

> The eye itself cannot
> Report;
> Perhaps, the eye
> Is, therefore,
> Least fit to see
> The Descent.

I feel refreshed. I have no regrets that I cannot or have not seen. For, seen at one point of time, you tend to forget it at another. Temporal dimensions have a way of getting totally limited in time. The advent is in time but of timelessness. Hence transcendence of time is the lense which registers that which represents both time and timelessness harmonised in moments of awareness.

That the Presence should announce its awareness to no one around at the moment of its advent fills me with a sense of harmony. Many see him now but do they?

The answer is working itself out in strange ways....

35

KALI'S CHILD

The village is intoxicating to me. Every object there fills me with wonder. Everyone in and of the village seems my kin for centuries. A feeling of having been together rarely leaves me. The feeling is instinctive, immediate. I try many times to ferret out the reason but no reason surfaces. The felt instinct in the guts is real: it stays and since it stays I have to convince myself of its stay through reason. How pathetic! What is felt as real constantly needs the scaffolding of reason!

Does reason show me what I see now as so palpable—show me things which it cannot see or show. I free myself from the grip of *buddhi*. The pythonic grip of *buddhi* gives way to the leaping-frog movement of the interior serpent. Once the transcendence is complete, the serpent sings with ease, with throat rapturously melodious.

I can hardly understand the movement. The movement of the serpent, I mean. One minute it is drowsy, down in the dumps and sleeps like an opium-drugged one. Full of inertia so total that it can hardly register even depression. To register even something negative you do require awareness. That the coiled being lacks.

But, unawares, in a split second it rouses itself—the entire body flexes itself. Blood begins to course through the veins, the warm glow of blood charges it with radiance. It uncoils in a moment that the movement itself hardly understands. "You require just one matchstick not the entire box of matches to light a lamp," he says.

Yes, I know, I experience. The movement of the energy floods the eyes. Like words which tug at you once you learn to recognise the letters, energy floods the eye and the eye speaks with the tongue of ineffable realities.

Thus I see the boy roaming in the streets of the village. He gets hold of a few cronies of his ilk. Bright, unspoilt by parents and teachers, they roam as the wind. "It bloweth where it listeth." They are quite a gang. Not defiant or disobedient. They hardly know the words. They hardly know that they could be guilty of disobedience. They obey only one they know—the only one they love and live for. Thus the question of disobeying any one else hardly arises.

In the group how radiant he appears! With locks of long hair falling gracefully over the face; the face lighted up with the smile that only he knows the secret of. (Others only know and see that smile. They hardly know the secret that makes it the smile that that smile is!) The bunch of boys which surrounds him—I hardly guess or know where they have been gathered from. Are they from his village? Are they school boys who, like him, play truant to school and roam as they like? Or does he get them out of the Void when he requires them and sends them back to the Void where they belong, once the need is over?

There is that one who sits near but hardly speaks a word. Fixed on him are his eyes; he has eyes for nothing, no one else. Those dark, bright eyes dancing with irrepressible joy have him as the object. He is the one who tells me: "Experience in silence whatever he shows, speaks, does! And then you know the splendour. Secret and silence know the secret, experience it in the cave of the heart; and relish it in silence. That is the only way he is relished and relishable."

He ought to know. Born only a few hours after the Presence heralds its advent, he should know. He tells me secrets that amaze me, secrets that engulf me with confirmation of what all I suspect about the Presence. He is a child: that is what he is. A child dear to the Child. With those big, dark eyes he watches him in sheer ecstasy.

And the other one. He is so joyous that it is difficult for tears to resist him! They well up in the eyes even as they flood his heart. He is charged with love. Every nerve centre in his body is deranged—with love for him. He is literally his shadow, his charioteer, his guide and friend. Guide? Yes. Guide to him in conducting him to places where he wishes to go. Constant recurrence of his name on this man's lips gets transferred even to paper: he goes on writing his Lord's name on pieces of paper. To be used by the Lord. (And the Lord uses them, no mistake about it.)

Between these two I learn things. Listen and learn and lie low for those things which passing through my being emerge in blazing visions. I do not know when and where. Not often but certainly in dreams, too.

Thus I see him with his mates roaming and roaming all over the village. Without any aim, without any goal. Just be and roam. Observe everything that strikes him as the evident rhythm of the Mother's Presence. A flock of cranes is enough. He will jump, leap into spaces no human with merely human consciousness has gone. The rustling of the leaves is the chiming of anklets on the lotus feet of Mother. The waves in the lake gently rising and falling are the breathing rhythm of the entire cosmos imaged in the Mother's heart.

He startles me when he sees a dog. Enough for it to stray before him. Instantly he goes to her. That is no surprise. This I am used to by now. But what unnerves me ('unnerving' is the signal that the serpent is shedding the sloth of despondency!) is what follows: "Ma! I know you wish to converse in this way. All mouths that speak are yours. So Ma, I listen! Do talk to me through this form of yours!" What follows is equally unnerving. His ears perk; he is all attention. And what this form says my ears can never register. What they do register is his laughter. Laughing and laughing! What does that dog say? Your guess is as good as mine!

Anything is enough for him to be alert. (Does he require anything as a stimulus to be aware? I wish I knew!) I see him watching the moonlight on a full moon day. I watch him but hardly know what he watches!

And how he strayed into that group of pundits I hardly could see. I must have been dozing. Or lost in reverie as quite often I am. His tender body with the graceful face I visualise; sharply in contrast. To the hardened faces of famed but foolish scholars. Wrangling over something I could hardly hear. Rather, I do not care to hear. Ears that hear in the heart the music of the Swan flapping its wings—do they wish to hear anything else? They shout at each other. I ignore it. They abuse one another over a *shastra*, I give it a deaf ear. (My ear perennially deaf to these things of late!)

They seem to come very near to blows. This part I like. Morbid? To enjoy others coming to blows. I know it is morbid. But then Mother has so many moods and modes. Meant for us: this *lila* of hers. Meant for us to keep distance and enjoy. I do. I am alert now as he is. His studied casualness slips. I know he is listening alertly—to arguments that threaten to settle themselves by blows. He is obviously enjoying the *tamasha*. But absorbing everything implicit in the *tamasha*.

All the boys are more or less silent. They look at each other in dismay. Particularly the one who always hangs around him. He is positively baffled. He never sees him in this role. As a singer, he is overwhelmed when he sings. As a sculptor whatever he chisels, this fellow sees with all eyes. Whenever he acts (but when does he not?) this chap forgets even to blink. And when he settles in the puja to see the Mother, this one is more or less lost—he watches him literally dead to everything else.

And I now watch as this chap does. And in a second he sidles up to a pundit. Whispers something in his ear. A strange look comes into the face of the pundit. He peers into the radiant boy's face. Disbelief is writ large on his face. With great difficulty he breaks into words: "See this child! Hardly the age to know the *sastras*. And he whispers gently what we are boisterously arguing about. And he has given the solution that makes all our arguments evaporate like foam!" What he tells the pundit and how they get the answer to their vexed debate hardly interests me. The ending of the debate of the scholars is what fascinates me.

The ending of the debate is the beginning of the burgeoning of love for him. That is what matters to me. And that matter makes for enactment of a unique nature. The eyes of a scholar in the group are shot with unusual radiance. They are quivering with unshed tears. A strange glow suffuses the face. Something that is revelatory comes to that glow. And he detaches himself from the others and literally engulfs the boy in his bear hug! What he sees in the boy—Kali's child—and what the boy allows him to see— they detach themselves from history. Get enshrined in words that are poetry. Poetry that is revelation. And a revelation that has no speech except words, words that have no other form than a poem. The scholar is obviously no mere scholar. Charged with the veracity of the truth he sees in the face of the Child, the words remain indelibly imprinted:

The Eternal Child
You are,
There are no
Farewells or
Fare forwards
For your advent
And withdrawal;
Only music fills
The spheres of the sky
With your eternal
Resurrection, your
Perennial renewal.
Apparently absent
You are eternally
Present!
Playing hide and
Seek in the secret
Garden of my heart,
You nestle
In the cradle
That the cosmos
Is for you!

The scholar poet kneels in adoration before the child being rocked in the cradle!

36
THE CROSS DANCES

Panchavati no longer attracts him. Incredible, but true. I can only watch. Curiosity, even, does not needle me these days. I look to only lying on the banks of the river. With him in the vicinity. I ensure that he stays in the eyelids. That is the one thing I am desperate about. To arrest him in the eye and rest in him. To cease doing everything else so that I seize him.

"Are you not repeating yourself?" you say. "Yes, I am." And I like recurrence more than anything else. Things recur, beings recur, nature itself is an endless cycle of recurrence. Renewal and recurrence are what I like most. Otherwise would I witness this recurrence and re-visioning....

"I seem to like him these days more than anyone else," he whispers gently. Wistfully I must say. Lying in that intense darkness and loving the Black One, the Dark One—these I am familiar with. Not this strange new mood. Of course, he is unpredictable. That I seem to know. He is even voracious: every god, every goddess must pass through his eye. And leave their residue so that the eye bursts forth in full splendour. The total spectrum of heavenly colours he wants to adorn his head with. Tell him about a new god and he would not leave until that god is got hold of and made to sink into his heart!

"Even Mother seems to lose her hold!" he continues. No regret or nostalgia. Only statement of fact. "That One enchants me! He seems to beckon to me! Irresistible. I am simply engulfed!" He is seized with the mood the symptoms of which I seem to be familiar with. Tremendous restlessness rouses the eternally active serpent. Its hood hisses with the fire of longing. His body's breath flows with a rhythm that sets his whole being in harmony with the vision of the One he longs for!

I am helpless. I hardly know who this One is. So many are there—many behind this One. I find it not an easy thing to fix who this One is. But I wait. Seeing him is enough for me. What or when he wants to see or seize is interesting to me. But largely immaterial. If you catch him and thereby everyone else is caught then why bother about the others. To catch this One is to catch everyone else!

How effortlessly he tunes me. Even as I lie there beside him—looking for whom I do not know—music floods my being. Music that engulfs me when in his presence I plunge into the river the first time. And the music and the song are not of the Mother. Strange, isn't it! That he should make me hear songs that are captivating but not of the Mother I know. This is intriguing but the songs are indelible. I hear them now, vast spaces crumble into nothing and the music floods me. Pours into my being. (That too, in alphabets I hardly know!)

On the banks
Of the river,
I listen to songs
That are alien
But are not
Unfamiliar
The song of this
Bird is shaped
By his beak!

'Beak' that is a bell! Surely he once made a strange remark: "His beak is unlike any of the pictures you see!" Baffled I put down this remark to his usual whimsy! And now the song surfaces in imperishable rhythm:

"Creator of the stars of night
the people's everlasting light,
redeemer, Saviour of us all,
O hear your servants when they call.

As once through Mary's flesh you came,
To save us from sin and shame,
So now, Redeemer, by your grace,
Come heal again our fallen race.
And when on that last judgment day
We rise to glory from decay,
Then come again O Saviour blest,
And bring us to eternal rest."
Memory-serpent uncoils herself. Yes, I know. At least now.
What he longs for. Longs for with all his heart and soul. Heart and
soul from whom the Mother voluntarily lets herself out. So that
the Son shall find his niche. The effortless sequence enchants me.
Yes, yes, yes—I cry exulting in this discovery of recurrence.
Recurrence that I read about but now revels in my eye in its unique
splendour.

I long for the Son
As I do for my
Virgin Mother!
Until I clasp the Son
To my bosom,
The mother inside
Threatens to fly
—in search of her
Son.

I catch them both. That is my luck. Real, palpable luck. There
is now no end to what I see. No end to what gets renewed. The
Eternal Present strikes me with a blow. A blow that, with
excruciatingly delightful pain, lays the past and the future flat. His
voice mesmerises me:

I long for him,
I long for my
Older brother!
Born of the same
Mother, time
Threatens to separate
Us. But I know
I devour time!

I am the Son,
He is the Father!
What is this thing that is hanging round my neck? It is no
vision. I feel it on the skin: its touch is so soothing. Like his touch.
Touch that soothes the about-to-strike serpent. But what is this
object hanging in my neck? Gleaming white, silver! Glowing even
in the darkness of the Dark One. Like a serpent round the neck of
the One who likes to have her as his pendent!
I gaze and gaze at the thing. Stupid, naive, full of
forgetfulness. Suddenly reduced to a clod in that Potter's hands.
Why doesn't he say what this is? He sure is eyeing it. Sure, feeling
its texture in his fingers, though strangely it is round my throat! He
winks at me mischievously; smiles in a way that you could hardly
miss the compassion behind the smile. And when he smiles like
that I know the result. With that smile on the face his voice puts in
words what the flesh is crazed with fear to touch (so unworthy we
are!) And the revelation comes gently; the words couch it in
caressing tones:
"Lord,
Who at this hour
When the whole world was shrouded in darkness
Mounted the wood of this cross
As the innocent victim for our redemption,
Give us always that light
Which will being us to eternal life
Who live and reign for ever and ever."
"And that is what I placed in your hands and now is in your
heart!" he adds. So plain he has to be for me, the Stupid One, to
see! But do I see right?
Where is the river bank? It recedes. The water is no longer
there. Or, rather it gives way. The steeple of the Church slowly
rises in and from the waters. The body of the Loved One, the
Church surfaces to show her dazzling beauty. I can hardly vouch
for what I see. How could I be worthy of this transfiguration?
Humility lashes at me like a whipcord. I cringe in fear. I hardly
dare to look at anything. But I gather the courage—the courage to
be and see straight ahead. He holds my hand. And leads me inside

his home. The church is dancing in ecstasy. She is blushing like a
bride at the Beloved's return. His home is now mine. He bends
slightly (you know I am short) and whispers:

Look! How
Radiant the Mother
Is! She welcomes
Me in this, the
Form and frame
She likes!
She constantly tells:
"Mother and daughter
father and son
do change their roles!"

Resurrected, I gaze at the Mother-Son, the Father-Daughter.
The Cross dances like a crazed serpent on my neck! "Isn't it your
birthday?" he asks with that twinkle in the eye that all eyes are
made for seeing!

THE WAVE THAT ENGULFS AND BEARS YOU AWAY

"It seems you said you are unborn, *ayonija*...," I ask him with hesitant eagerness. Hesitant, since I asked him once already. No streak of hesitation crosses his face. "I did not say it. I wrote it in my hand. And, of course, I do not have your flair for writing...," he teases me as usual. "I am supposed to be illiterate. But somehow I manage to spell out what I wish to say."

I look far into the advancing night. A rainbow forms round the emerging full-moon. O rarely saw such a thing. The sheer radiance is enough: nothing else is needed. He is surpassingly luminous, clutches a pillow nestling in his lap—as if that ties him down to the earth. But, then, the cotton inside is the same. Only the shape and the colour of the pillows differ.

"Cosmically introduced," the words startle me. He gently whispers the words: as if the four corners of the earth may not be able to hold the import of the words. "Cosmically introduced," I repeat the words, the two words that hold the beginning and the end, the end and the beginning. The ceaseless flux and the eternality amaze me. "*Avatara!*" the words cross my lips involuntarily. "Does it matter what words you use? After all the sign is not the destination, the name is not the named," he says.

"But I wish to talk about it. I am fascinated that I see it in flesh and blood. Can't I share it with other?" "You do whatever you like. So long as you don't implicate me in anything you say or do!" he says with playful (almost sly) seriousness.

So it came to pass: on the eve of Christmas. He came in an unexpectedly expected way (usual with him.) I hardly know who

sent word: many throng to see him, hear him (if possible), bask,
surely, in the sheer warmth of his Presence. But make no mistake.
Many, perhaps, were called but few (the chosen ones?) came. A
silence that speaks more than speech hung all over. As if nature
shielded, cordoned off, all 'profanity'. Joy writ large on the faces
spoke its own language.

My usual bantering tone flew away like a bird long held in the
cage. I never knew I could be serious in this way. A lump in the
throat seized me. Tears and terror at what I plan to speak fought
with each other. Terror? Yes, yes. Is it fun to summon words to
say things about the One behind the Many, the Many behind the
One, the envisioned Being? But I know, too, that

> The Cosmic strength
> Of that love-radiation
> Inundates my being
> And moulding me
> Into the Master's mouthpiece, manages
> To catch the Mother's
> *Matrikas* as they
> Fly: live sparks from
> Her luminous anvil!

Thus I began

> Do you love Jesus?
> You seek Krishna's grace?
> Wish to sport in the
> Radiant loveliness of Sri Rama?
> Attempt to scale the
> Heights of renunciation
> To catch a glimpse of Siva?
> Wonder whether it is
> Possible for Yasoda and Ram
> To give a glimpse of
> Their strangely composite cosmic form?

> Do all these appear incredible?
> But there are more:
> Shirdi Sai

Satya Sai
Ramana, Ramakrishna
Aurobindo...
Many behind the One and
The One behind the many...
You think all these
Cannot come together
Dancing in ecstasy
In the Self-same Being?
Then look at
The unanimously
Anonymous being,
Hiding his radiant eternity,
Sporting with us
In a slyly concealed way!
No outward sing
Escapes to signal
His splendour!
No self-declarations
From This One!
No startling revelations
To rouse and rattle you:
Gently, ever so gently,
He reveals and re-veils
Himself: if 'Sri Ram'
Is visible, Sri Krishna
Is in the vicinity:
If Sri Krishna, the Playful One,
Teases you, Sri Rama tilts
His eyelids at you from behind!
From the corner of the eye (threatening to exchange tears for
sight) I watch him: do I catch a glimpse of affirmation! Do I see
just a flicker of the eyelids in fond approval? A gentle clearing of
the throat to keep in check the tidal waves of all-embracing love?
A smile that ceaselessly dances on the lips, strangely, in a bizarre
moment of surreal reality (the only Real that really is),

transforming itself into an aura that envelops everyone, everything?

Humankind cannot bear reality very much! Some weep uncontrollably; some laugh, laugh in that ridiculous way that sages do enormous penance to learn! Some simply sit and stare. Breathless moments when twilight suffuses both form and language. And strangest of all things: unless you see you cannot believe it (and I saw!): a group of birds come, in a split second, rushing to the closed glass window pane. They peck at the glass fiercely: as if they could break the glass and enter to greet him. They must have flown all the way from Kamarpukur to the Town of Truth which he makes his abode now! ('Love Birds' he says!) And he jumps to the window. The familiar look appears on the face. In the silence that follows I clear my throat and chant:

Dear!
You are the Ancient One
Filling the fathomless heart
With frontierless, fiery yet fond
Flood of love!
You are the Cosmic Miracle-Mother
The Tireless Traveller,
Throwing the pearls of
Your Passion all over!
You are, in this loveless land,
The Outsider-looking
Insider, engulfing everything
In the cosmic sweep of your ceaseless love!
You are the Paramatman,
The Paramahamsa
The Swan that sports
In the perennial waters
Of pure, limpid passion!
Mother-Lover Thou Art
And So shall you remain!
"Sir Ramakrishna."

"Is your rhapsody over, dear?" he pulls me back gently. The Ganga winks at me: "I am a privy to your words and your vision,"

she whispers. I look for him: where is he? I heard his voice, I
know. But where is he? "Form hardly matters, dear!" (Even slips
in printing: at one point I actually see "Sri? Ramakrishna!") The
wordless voice stays with me.

> The boat responds
> To the gay breeze.
> I loll in its bosom;
> The lulling waters
> Bear me away...
> I nestle under the
> Kalpataru: the Wish-Yielding
> Mother watches me
> In the shade of Her
> Unblinking Eyelids.
> The Love-lense
> breaks the camera,
> leaps into
> *childakasha*...

AFTERWORD

The envisioned "Sri Ram": born in 1957, makes Nizamabad in Andhra Pradesh his *lila kshetra*. My (pre-and-well-determined) encounters with him made the distinction between the visual and the visionary a tiresome cliché. His "lenses" made "Sri Ramakrishna" (literally) an elder brother of his. I now seem to know what it is to love—more than know—"Sri Ramakrishna" I hardly, then, know where the Divine Twins begin and end!

A ceaseless flow of experience (tangible, palpable) shapes itself into words. "Re-visioning Ramakrishna" is the "final" volume of three in the making. *One Behind the Many* and *Many Behind the One* are the other two. When they emerge into being depends on Their grace.... (The first a sobering account running into 2100 pages in writing is completed.)

"Sri Ram" has his own ways of making himself known. Nevertheless, anyone who feels that s/he would know more about this unanimously anonymous person may refer to *Viveka Sravanti: Letters for Seekers of Peace, Dewdrops On a Lotus Leaf* and *In Search of Mother: A Biography of "Sri Ram"* (all from Sterling, 1997 and 1998)

Finally, this is also, in a sense, for the one who shares my passion for Paramahamsa and 'Sri Ram'. She made the transition from the one to the other an act of grace, of felt love...

MSR